100 MATHS HOMEWORK

RENEWED PRIMARY FRAMEWORK

MR. I. M. FORSYTH.

100 MATHS HOMEWORK ACTIVITIES

YEAR 6

John Davis, Julie Dyer, Sonia Tibbatts and Richard Cooper

Credits

Authors
John Davis, Julie Dyer,
Sonia Tibbatts, Richard Cooper

Development Editor
Nicola Morgan

Assistant Editor
Margaret Eaton

Illustrations
Mike Phillips (Beehive Illustration)
Phil Garner (Beehive Illustration)

Series Designer
Helen Taylor

Designer
Macmillan Publishing Solutions

Mixed Sources
Product group from well-managed
forests and other controlled sources
www.fsc.org   Cert no. TT-COC-002769
© 1996 Forest Stewardship Council
FSC

Text © John Davis, Julie Dyer,
Sonia Tibbatts and Richard Cooper
© 2009 Scholastic Ltd

Designed using Adobe InDesign

Published by Scholastic Ltd
Villiers House
Clarendon Avenue
Leamington Spa
Warwickshire CV32 5PR

www.scholastic.co.uk

Printed by Bell and Bain Ltd, Glasgow

1 2 3 4 5 6 7 8 9   9 0 1 2 3 4 5 6 7 8

British Library Cataloguing-in-Publication Data
A catalogue record for this book is available from the British Library.

ISBN 978-1407-10221-4

The rights of John Davis, Julie Dyer, Sonia Tibbatts and Richard Cooper to
be identified as the authors of this work have been asserted by them in
accordance with the Copyright, Designs and Patents Act 1988.

Extracts from the Primary National Strategy's *Primary Framework for
Mathematics* (2006) www.standards.dfes.gov.uk/primaryframework © Crown
copyright. Reproduced under the terms of the Click Use Licence.

Contents

Introduction **4-5**

Homework diary **6**

Homework

Homework: Counting, partitioning and calculating

Teachers' notes. **7-8**

Homework sheets **9-20**

Homework: Securing number facts, understanding shape

Teachers' notes. **21-22**

Homework sheets **23-40**

Homework: Handling data and measures

Teachers' notes. **41-42**

Homework sheets **43-54**

Homework: Calculating, measuring and understanding shape

Teachers' notes. **55-56**

Homework sheets **57-68**

Homework: Securing number facts, relationships and calculating

Teachers' notes. **69-70**

Homework sheets **71-88**

Puzzles and problems

Objectives grid **89**

Activities. **90-107**

Answers

Homework answers. **108-110**

Puzzles and problems answers **111**

About the series

100 Maths Homework Activities offers a complete solution to your planning and resourcing for maths homework activities. There are six books in the series, one for each year group from Year 1 to Year 6.

Each *100 Maths Homework Activities* book contains 72 homework activities, which cover the Renewed Framework objectives, and 36 puzzles and problems, which focus on the Using and applying objectives.

About the homework activities

Each homework activity is presented as a photocopiable page, with some supporting notes for parents and carers provided underneath the activity.

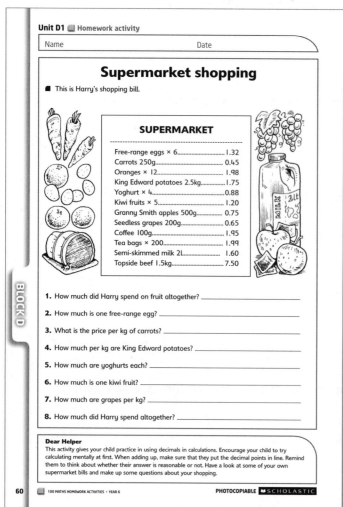

Teachers' notes relating to the activities appear in grid format at the beginning of each block's activities. When exactly the homework is set and followed up is left to your professional judgement.

Across the *100 Maths Homework Activities* series, the homework activities cover a range of homework types. Some of the activities are for sharing. These encourage the child to discuss the homework task with a parent or carer, and may, for example, involve the home context, or a game to be played with the carer. Other activities involve investigations or problem-solving tasks. Again, the parent or carer is encouraged to participate in the activity, offering support to the child, and discussing the activity and its outcomes with the child.

Using the homework activities

Each homework page includes a 'Helper note', which explains the aim of the homework and how the adult can support their child if he or she cannot get started. It is recommended that some form of homework diary be used alongside these activities, through which to establish an effective home-school dialogue about the children's enjoyment and understanding of the homework. A homework diary page is provided on page 6 of this book.

Teachers' notes

The teachers' notes appear in a grid format at the start of each block's homework activities. Each grid contains the following information:

- the Framework unit
- the homework activity's title
- a brief description of the format and content of the activity, which will help you to decide which homework activity to choose
- the Renewed Framework learning objective/s
- a 'Managing the homework' section which provides two types of help – 'before' and 'after'. The 'before' notes provide suggestions for ways to introduce and explain the homework before the children take it home. These notes might include a brief oral activity to undertake as preparation for the homework. The 'after' notes provide suggestions for how to manage the review of the homework when the children return with it to school. Suggestions include discussing strategies used for solving a problem, comparing solutions, and playing a game as a class.

About the puzzles and problems

The puzzles and problems (pages 90-107) provide coverage of the Using and applying mathematics objectives and can be used very flexibly to provide children with a comprehensive range of fun maths tasks to take home. The grid displayed on page 89 shows which puzzles and problems cover each of the Using and applying objectives.

Puzzles and problems

29 Battle of the bands

The new bands Kneecap and Ankle are performing concerts.

Kneecap charge £1.25 a ticket and 175 people come to their concert.

Ankle charge £1.35 a ticket and 160 people come to their concert.

Which band takes the most money and by how much?

30 Fruit punch

Freya makes a fruit punch for three people. She uses:

1½ litres lemonade

4 oranges

3 limes

200g sugar

300g strawberries

Rewrite the recipe so there is enough fruit punch for nine people.

104   ◻ 100 MATHS HOMEWORK ACTIVITIES · YEAR 6   PHOTOCOPIABLE ◻SCHOLASTIC

The puzzles and problems are based on work that the children will be covering during the year and should test their skills at that level. Some of the questions may be solved quickly, others will require more thought. Either way, children should be encouraged to try a variety of different approaches to solving problems and to look for clues and patterns in maths. It is essential for them to read the question carefully (sometimes more than once) to understand exactly what they are being asked to do. A few of the puzzles and problems will require an everyday household item or the help of a family member. Most should be readily solved by a child working on their own.

Remind the children that if a problem or puzzle is proving too difficult or frustrating, they could leave it and come back to it later with a refreshed mind!

Developing a homework policy

The homework activities have been written with the DCSF 'Homework guidelines' in mind. These can be located in detail on the Standards website **www.standards.dfes.gov. uk/homework/goodpractice** The guidelines are a good starting point for planning an effective homework policy. Effective home-school partnerships are also vital in ensuring a successful homework policy.

Encouraging home-school links

An effective working partnership between teachers and parents and carers makes a positive impact upon children's attainment in mathematics. The homework activities in this book are part of that partnership. Parents and carers are given guidance on what the homework is about, and on how to be involved with the activity. There are suggestions for helping the children who are struggling with a particular concept, such as ways of counting on or back mentally, and extension ideas for children who would benefit from slightly more advanced work.

The homework that is set across the curriculum areas for Year 6 should amount to a total of about two and a half hours a week. The homework diary page, which can be sent home with the homework activity with opportunities for a response from the parents/carers, can be found on page 6 of this book.

Using the activities with *100 Maths Framework Lessons Year 6*

The activities covered in this book fit the planning within the book *100 Maths Framework Lessons Year 6* (also published by Scholastic Ltd). As teachers plan their work on a week-by-week basis, so the homework activities can be chosen to fit the appropriate unit of work.

Name of activity & date sent home	Child's comments		Helper's comments	Teacher's comments
	Did you like this activity? Draw a face. 😊 🙂 ☹️ a lot a little not much	How much did you learn? Draw a face. 😊 🙂 ☹️ a lot a little not much		

Counting, partitioning and calculating

Activity name	Learning objectives	Managing the homework
A1		
Divide me Estimate first, then divide a number by U or TU to reach a given target.	Use approximations, inverse operations and tests of divisibility to estimate and check results	**Before:** Remind the children of the importance of estimating before carrying out calculations. **After:** Check through some of the children's answers. How did estimating first help them to decide which pair of numbers to divide?
Positive and negative Use a number line to solve number sequence problems involving positive and negative integers.	Find the difference between a positive and a negative integer, or two negative integers	**Before:** Revise positive/negative number work. Remind the children to use the number line to physically count the steps. **After:** Work through the answers. Which problems did the children find easiest/hardest? Discuss everyday uses of positive/negative numbers.
Guitar Genius Order decimals with up to three places in the context of a computer game.	Order decimals with up to three places, and position them on the number line	**Before:** Brief the children on the technique for ordering decimals. **After:** Check the answers with the class. Discuss any problems encountered.
Decimal dash! Multiply and divide decimals in the context of a speed test.	Use knowledge of place value and multiplication facts to 10×10 to derive related multiplication and division facts involving decimals (for example, 0.8×7, $4.8 \div 6$)	**Before:** Tell the children that they will use their knowledge of multiplication and related division facts to complete this activity. **After:** Go through the answers and compare times for successfully completed tests.
A2		
One of each Pair numbers and multiply them on the calculator to find given totals.	• Solve problems involving decimals; choose and use appropriate calculation strategies, including calculator use • Use a calculator to solve problems	**Before:** Explain that one number has to be taken from each set of shapes to make the given total. Encourage the children to make a sensible guess first. Check that calculators are available at home. **After:** Check through the solutions. How accurate were the estimates? How did the estimates help the children to find the correct numbers?
On the grid Approximate first and then use the grid method to work through examples of HTU × TU.	Use efficient written methods to multiply three-digit integers by a two-digit integer	**Before:** Ensure that the children fully understand the grid method. Work through the example on the sheet. **After:** Discuss the advantages and disadvantages of the grid method. How does it compare with other methods the children have tried?
What's missing? Look carefully at word problems and decide what information needs to be added in order to find each solution. Complete the calculations using own information.	Solve multi-step problems and problems involving decimals; choose and use appropriate calculation strategies at each stage, including calculator use	**Before:** Revise the step-by-step approach used for solving problems. Remind the children that they will have to provide some of their own numbers to find the solution. **After:** Check through the information the children provided themselves. How many variations are there for each question? Discuss the methods used to find solutions.
Missing digits Substitute missing digits in number sentences involving decimal numbers.	Use efficient written methods to multiply and divide integers and decimals by a one-digit integer, and to multiply two-digit and three-digit integers by a two-digit integer	**Before:** Ensure that the children have a clear understanding of the four operations using decimal numbers. Talk to them about finding missing numbers, often using the inverse operation. **After:** Go through the questions and discuss the various strategies the children used. How did they check their answers?

Counting, partitioning and calculating

Activity name	Learning objectives	Managing the homework
A3		
Nearest wins Multiply HTU by U to reach a given Th or H target number.	Use efficient written methods to multiply integers by a one-digit integer, and to multiply three-digit integers by a two-digit integer	**Before:** Remind the children of the different ways they can multiply: grid method; partitioning; standard format. Discuss how digits can be arranged to try to 'hit' a target number. (A large target number would need a high digit in the H column.) **After:** Choose two targets from the homework sheet and ask the children for the calculations they performed. Who was nearest to the target?
Swamp fever Add several HTU numbers and subtract pairs of ThHTU numbers in the context of a trek through a swamp.	Use efficient written methods to add and subtract integers	**Before:** Revise the standard methods of addition and subtraction. Emphasise the importance of setting out digits in the correct columns. **After:** Choose two calculations from each section. Ask half the class to use a standard method of calculation and the other half an alternative method (for example, an empty number line). Which method is the most efficient?
Shop 'til you drop In this shopping game, players move around a grid buying food. A running total of amount spent and balance left is kept.	Solve multi-step problems and problems involving decimals; choose and use appropriate calculation strategies at each stage, including calculator use	**Before:** Demonstrate how to keep a simple balance sheet to record how much money is left: Spent Balance £5 £1.65 £3.35 **After:** Discuss outcomes. What was the least amount of articles that could be bought with £15? Did anyone complete their shopping by buying this amount?

| Name | Date |

Divide me

▪ Use your division skills to hit the target.

▪ Choose a number from each bag.

▪ Use any division method to make a number from the target board.

▪ Estimate first, as it will help you choose the correct pair of numbers. The first has been done for you.

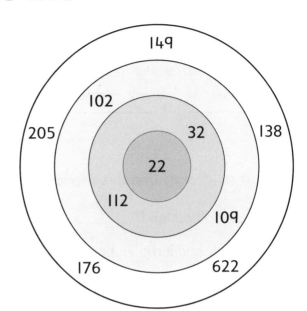

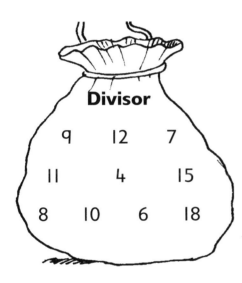

Divisor

9   12   7

11   4   15

8   10   6   18

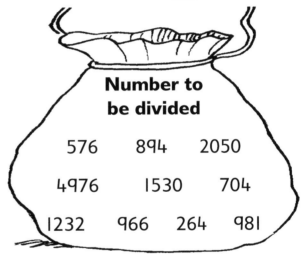

Number to be divided

576   894   2050

4976   1530   704

1232   966   264   981

$\begin{array}{r} 109 \\ 9\overline{)\,981} \end{array}$				

Dear Helper

It is important that the children look carefully at each set of numbers and estimate mentally which pair will make the target number. Each number can only be used once. The first two digits of the number to be divided are the most significant to help with estimating, as it will give the first digit of the target number.

BLOCK A

Name

Date

Positive and negative

🔳 Use the number line to help you solve these problems.

–10 –9 –8 –7 –6 –5 –4 –3 –2 –1 0 1 2 3 4 5 6 7 8 9 10

1. Start at –5 and jump three spaces in a positive direction.

Where do you land? _____

2. Start at 4 and jump eight spaces in a negative direction.

Where do you land? _____

3. Start at 9 and jump fifteen spaces in a negative direction.

Where do you land? _____

4. Moving in a positive direction, give the next three numbers in this sequence.

–9   –6   –3   ⬜ ⬜ ⬜

5. Moving in a negative direction, give the next three numbers in this sequence.

10   6   2   ⬜ ⬜ ⬜

6. Put these numbers in order of size, starting with the largest.

–3 –1 4 0 6 2 _____

7. Put these numbers in order of size, starting with the smallest.

0 5 –4 –2 7 –8 _____

🔳 Make up some questions of your own about positive and negative numbers on the back of the sheet for your helper to complete.

Dear Helper
The number line provided at the top of the sheet will be useful for children who prefer to count the steps physically in order to find answers. Reinforce that moving in a positive direction goes to the right and moving in a negative direction goes to the left. As an extension, write down a pair of numbers from the number line and ask your child to put the 'less than' or 'greater than' signs (< and >) between them (for example, –2 < 1 and 3 > 0).

PHOTOCOPIABLE 🔳SCHOLASTIC

Name   Date

Guitar Genius

◀ These are the scores achieved by five children playing the console game *Guitar Genius*.

◀ Write each child's scores in order, smallest first.

Eric: 2.553, 5.552, 5.225, 2.225

Josh: 1.002, 2.101, 1.221, 0.202

Ganesh: 5.445, 4.554, 4.504, 5.545

Katy: 13.367, 13.673, 31.352, 13.763

Alesha: 32.332, 23.223, 33.323, 23.322

Dear Helper

This activity helps your child to order decimals. It is helpful if you look at the decimal numbers with your child and identify how much each digit is worth. For example, 4.753 is four whole numbers, seven tenths, five hundredths and three thousandths. When your child orders the decimals, they should start reading their size from the left and work towards the right.

BLOCK A

Name   Date

Decimal dash!

◾ Use your knowledge of place value and multiplication facts up to 10 × 10 to answer these questions. Time yourself, then try again to see if you can beat your record!

1. 0.3 × 5 _____

2. 0.6 × 4 _____

3. 0.8 × 7 _____

4. 0.9 × 3 _____

5. 0.2 × 10 _____

6. 0.7 × 8 _____

7. 0.1 × 9 _____

8. 0.4 × 6 _____

9. 0.5 × 2 _____

◾ Now use your knowledge of division facts to answer these. Time yourself, then try again to see if you can beat your record!

10. 2.4 ÷ 6 _____

11. 3.6 ÷ 4 _____

12. 2.1 ÷ 7 _____

13. 4.8 ÷ 6 _____

14. 5.6 ÷ 8 _____

15. 3.5 ÷ 5 _____

16. 1.8 ÷ 3 _____

17. 8.1 ÷ 9 _____

18. 6.4 ÷ 8 _____

Dear Helper

This activity helps your child to realise that they can use known number facts to help with multiplication and division of decimals. Encourage your child to check their answers carefully. You could help by timing your child as they answer the questions and then asking them to beat their record. Only 100% correct answers will do!

Name	Date

One of each

◼ One number from the line of circles multiplied by one number from the line of triangles will complete each of the number sentences below.

◼ Estimate first and then find the missing numbers using your calculator. Use a separate sheet for estimates if you need to.

▢ Here is an example:

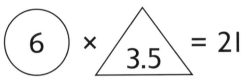

$$6 \times 3.5 = 21$$

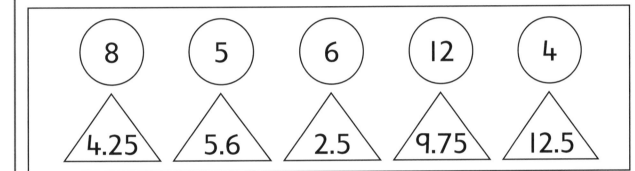

1. ◯ × △ = 20

2. ◯ × △ = 51

3. ◯ × △ = 39

4. ◯ × △ = 28

5. ◯ × △ = 75

6. ◯ × △ = 15

7. ◯ × △ = 100

8. ◯ × △ = 117

Dear Helper
Ensure that your child chooses one number from each set of shapes when they are trying to find the answers. Encourage them to make sensible estimates of the answer, before it is calculated, so that numerous random pairings do not have to be made. Check that your child is able to enter the correct numbers into the calculator, especially locating the position of the decimal point. Remind them that in a whole number the decimal point is located on the right-hand side.

Name   Date

On the grid

◼ This is a method of multiplying three-digit numbers by two-digit numbers using the grid system.

◼ Look carefully at the example below and make sure you understand the steps you need to follow. Remember to work out an approximate answer first.

325 × 47   Approximate: 300 × 50 = 15,000

✗	300	20	5	**Totals**
40	12000	800	200	13000
7	2100	140	35	2275
				15275

◼ Now work through these questions using the same grid method. Work out an approximate answer first, using a separate sheet of paper if you need to.

1. 245 × 47

✗				**Totals**

2. 592 × 27

✗				**Totals**

3. 765 × 58

✗				**Totals**

Dear Helper
This homework will help your child to practise a method of multiplying they have learned recently. Allow your child to work through this practice activity on their own. Then ask them to explain the process they have used and what they have done at each step. Your child should have worked out an approximate answer first each time. Check it with them and discuss the importance of doing this. Can they check their answers by using another method of multiplying or by using the inverse operation (dividing)?

Name	Date

What's missing?

🔳 There is an important piece of information missing from each of these word problems.

🔳 Working with someone, decide what information you need before the problems can be solved.

🔳 When you have decided what piece of information is missing, make up numbers for this part of the question and solve the problem. Show all your calculations on another piece of paper. Estimate each answer first and find a way of checking it afterwards.

1. 247 children join the school's Art Club. How many more are there in the Gym Club?

2. Alan, Sunil, Martha and Emma collect football cards. If Alan has 57 cards, Sunil 29 cards and Martha 63 cards, how many cards do the four children have altogether?

3. Maths lessons take place each day in school. How long do maths lessons last in total during a normal school week?

4. A farmer divides 345 sheep into equal numbers to put them into pens. How many sheep are there in each pen?

5. Stacey is training for a swimming race. She swims 500 metres every weekday, but more at weekends. How far does she swim in a complete week?

6. Fencing panels measure 1.60m in length and cost £19.99 each. How much will it cost to fence along one side of the garden?

Dear Helper

This activity is for you and your child to do together, as discussion is an important part of the task. Each problem is impossible without more information. Assist your child to come up with sensible suggestions for the missing piece of information. Ask them to tell you about the problem-solving step-by-step strategy they have been using in class to solve number problems like these. Your child could use a calculator to check their answers. Challenge them by working together to make up other problems of this kind.

Name   Date

Missing digits

■ Look at each of these calculations and work out the missing digits.

1. 2 ⬚ 3. ⬚ × 8 = 2188

2. 78.36 ÷ ⬚ = 26.12

3. 3.25 + 170.02 + 103.5 + ⬚ . ⬚ ⬚ = 282.64

4. 17.2 ⬚ × 7 = 1 ⬚ 0.96

5. ⬚ .12 ⬚ × 3 = 21.3 ⬚ 2

6. 6.9 ⬚ × 35 = 2 ⬚ 1.85

Dear Helper
Your child has been looking at calculations using decimal numbers. Encourage them to write the calculation in a column format to calculate the missing digits. Remind them that they should check that their answer is correct by substituting the digits into the questions and re-calculating. They may calculate the answer or they may use trial and improvement methods (which means that they estimate and see if their number 'fits' and then refine their estimate until the solution is reached).

Name	Date

Nearest wins

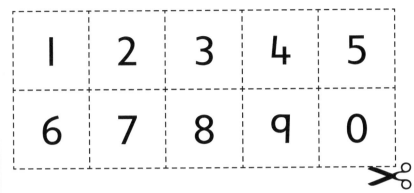

1	2	3	4	5
6	7	8	9	0

Target numbers	
1550	486
2500	6100
920	8000
1750	3200
5070	4400
7005	750
2010	2800
3550	

◀ Instructions – a game for two players

☐ Cut out the number cards and arrange them face down on the table.

☐ Each player should pick four cards and turn them face up.

☐ Each player chooses a target number from the box and arranges their own cards as a multiplication calculation to try and get as near as possible to the target number.

☐ For example: I pick numbers 3, 8, 4 and 9. I choose target number 1550 and arrange them to make the following calculation:

$$\begin{array}{r} 489 \\ \times \quad\ 3 \\ \hline 1467 \end{array}$$

Player 1	Player 2

◀ Scoring

☐ The player nearest their target number wins 5 points. The other player wins 1 point, if they are within 200 of their target number.

☐ Record your scores in the table on the right. The first player to achieve 25 points wins the game.

Dear Helper

Encourage your child to use mental methods to estimate what would be a realistic target number to choose. In particular, the digit chosen for the hundreds place will be significant, as this is the digit that will bring your child near to the target number. Answers greater than the target number are acceptable as it is the nearest to the target number that wins.

BLOCK A

Name   Date

Swamp fever

1. Professor Find-It and his assistant Doctor Dig-It-Up have been working deep in the jungle. Unfortunately, they have both come down with a bad case of swamp fever. They have managed to get back to the first aid centre, but need a little help getting to the medicine chest.

◻ In order to get to the medicine, they need to cross the river using the stepping stones.

◻ The stones they choose must add up to exactly 1000.

◻ Help them choose the correct stones to cross the river. (They don't have to use adjoining stones, they are allowed to jump to stones a little further away.)

◻ Colour in the ones that add up to exactly 1000.

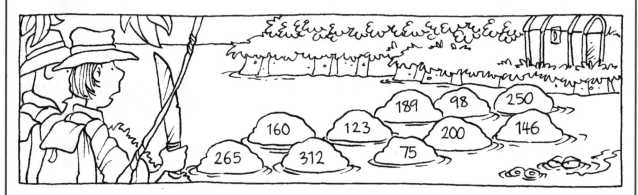

2. Now that they have crossed the river, they need help to open the medicine chest.

◻ They need to find out a secret code to open the chest.

◻ Work out the secret code by calculating the answers to these questions. Write each answer in the space provided.

◻ Good luck – the explorers are counting on you!

$$6483 - 1372$$

$$9023 - 4362$$

$$7001 - 4921$$

$$5091 - 3275$$

Dear Helper
Your child has used a variety of mental and pencil-and-paper methods for addition. Encourage them to use empty number lines and the column method as well as mental strategies, such as adding the hundreds, then the tens and then the units. Some children may prefer to start with 1000 and take away each amount, ending with zero. Ensure they keep a running total of the numbers they have used, so that adjustments can be made easily to find the correct stones. There are two possible solutions to question 1.

Name	Date

Shop 'til you drop (1)

◼ **You will need:** a dice; pencils; running total grid for each person; 'Shop 'til you drop' board (see page 20).

◼ **Instructions – a game for two or more players**

☐ Your task is to spend exactly £15 in the supermarket.

☐ As you travel round the board, buy items if you land on a space marked 'B'.

☐ If you land on a space marked 'P' you may put items back if you wish.

☐ Remember, you must spend exactly £15! There is a catch though – each player may only buy one of each item.

☐ Use a running total grid (see example below) to record your answers.

Item	Bought	Put back	Balance
			£15.00
Coffee	£3.30		£11.70
Meat	£7.60	£7.60	£11.70
Pineapple	£1.99		£9.71

Running total

Item	Bought	Put back	Balance
			£15.00

Dear Helper

Check that your child is able to use a balance sheet. Remind them that the balance is a running total of what they have spent. As your child moves around the board buying items, they may realise that their balance is not enough to buy another item to leave them with exactly nothing. They will need to put back an item to release more money into their balance.

Name   Date

Shop 'til you drop (2)

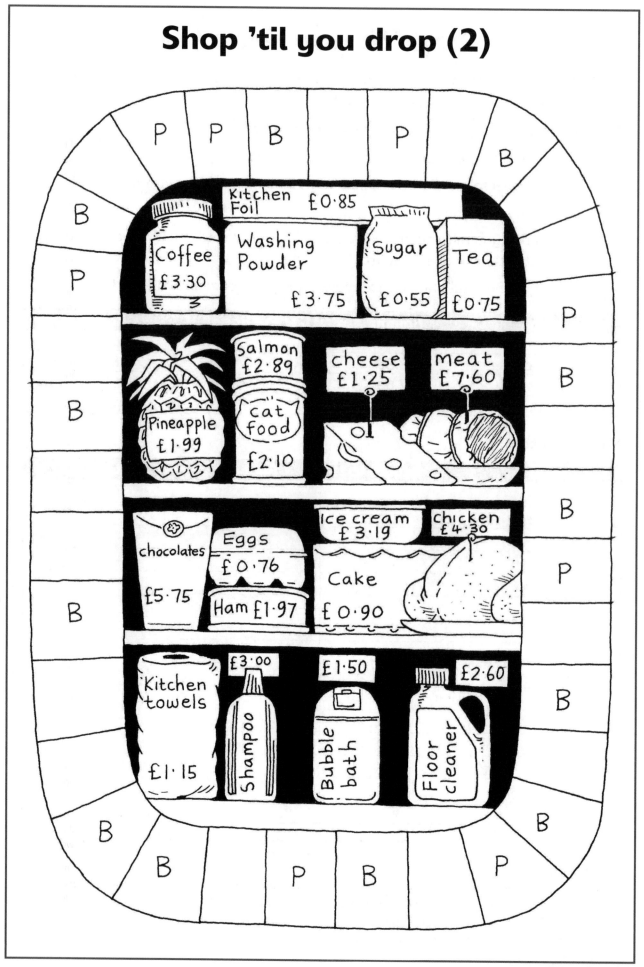

Securing number facts, understanding shape

Activity name	Learning objectives	Managing the homework
B1		
Multiplying and dividing Generate three-digit numbers to multiply or divide by 10/100/1000.	Use knowledge of place value and multiplication facts to derive related multiplication and division facts involving decimals	**Before:** Ensure that the children have a clear understanding of multiplication and division of three-digit numbers (including decimals) by 10/100/1000. Less able children should work with whole numbers only. **After:** Ask the children to share some of their results. Do the rest of the class agree?
Name that shape Work out hidden shapes according to a set of given properties.	Describe, identify and visualise parallel edges and use these to classify 2D shapes	**Before:** Remind the children of the properties used to classify shapes: angle, sides, symmetry. Remind them that some shapes share properties, and so all properties need to be taken into consideration before guessing the shape. **After:** Choose some of the shapes from the sheet. Ask the children for their properties. Which shapes have similar properties? How did they distinguish between these shapes?
What's next? Complete and make up number sequences, some with two operations in each step.	Represent and interpret sequences, patterns and relationships involving numbers	**Before:** Explain that some of the sequences may contain two operations in each step (for example, ×2 − 1). **After:** Ask the children to present their made-up number sequences to a partner. Can their partner solve each one and find the rule?
What's it worth? Basic algebra practice with algebraic statements to solve.	Represent and interpret relationships involving numbers; construct and use simple expressions and formulae in words then symbols	**Before:** Ensure that the children understand that they need to replace the letters in each calculation with given numbers. Explain that some may require them to perform a number of operations. For example: 7c + 3b = (7 × 7) + (3 × 3). **After:** Choose one or two of the algebraic statements. Ask the children to explain how they tackled each of them.
Fancy boxes Draw nets for a cube. Make different 3D shapes from 2D drawings.	Make and draw shapes with increasing accuracy and apply knowledge of their properties	**Before:** Ensure that the children can recognise a simple net for a cube and talk about different variations. **After:** How many different nets did the children find? Make a display of the different nets (there are 11). Check for duplication as children may have a reflection of a previous net.
Floor shapes Investigate tessellation of shapes to design a tile pattern for a floor.	Make and draw shapes with increasing accuracy and apply knowledge of their properties	**Before:** Discuss which regular shapes tessellate and then show some designs where irregular shapes are used. **After:** Make a display of the different shape patterns that children devise. Check that they do tessellate.
B2		
Boxed in Solve magic square puzzles by adding and subtracting whole numbers, decimal numbers, fractions and positive/negative numbers. Complete number chains based on adding consecutive numbers.	Tabulate systematically the information in a problem or puzzle; identify and record the steps or calculations needed to solve it	**Before:** Go through some examples of magic squares, explaining that each line (including the two diagonals) always add up to the same total. Magic squares are thought to have originated in China. Also explain the method used for completing the number chains. **After:** Check the solutions. Discuss the methods used. Which of the magic squares did children find most difficult? What strategies did they use with the number chains? Ask them to make up their own magic squares and number chains.
Euler's rule Use a variety of 3D shapes to prove a rule proposed 300 years ago by the Swiss mathematician Leonhard Euler.	Describe, identify and visualise edges or faces; use these properties to classify 3D solids	**Before:** Revise the properties of the main straight-sided 3D shapes. Check the children's understanding of key words such as *face*, *edge* and *vertex*. **After:** Check through the examples children have chosen and discuss if the rule applies to all straight-sided 3D shapes. Encourage children to find out more about Euler's work.
Letter time Solve number problems in which letters or shapes are used as symbols to indicate missing numbers.	Represent and interpret relationships involving numbers; construct and use simple expressions and formulae in words then symbols	**Before:** Go through some examples of this kind of number puzzle, especially reminding children that 5n is the usual way of writing 5 × n and that letters written over other letters or numbers indicates division. **After:** Work through the solutions with the class and iron out any problems that might have occurred.

BLOCK B

Activity name	Learning objectives	Managing the homework
Jumping frogs Work out the rule for each number sequence (both forwards and backwards) and then continue the sequence using the same pattern.	Represent and interpret sequences, patterns and relationships involving numbers	**Before:** Go through a number of two-step sequence patterns with the children to make sure they understand how to apply rules. **After:** Check that the rule for each sequence has been correctly identified. Investigate some of the sequences that children have produced themselves.
How old are they? Use information about the ages of members of a family to answer questions.	Tabulate systematically the information in a problem or puzzle; identify and record the steps or calculations needed to solve it, using symbols where appropriate; interpret solutions in the original context and check their accuracy	**Before:** Ensure that the children understand that they have to read the information and refer back to previous questions, making sure that the answer they give is what has been asked for. **After:** Ask which questions the children found tricky; most mistakes will be because the children have not read the questions carefully.
Build it Construct a solid shape by first calculating measurements of a combination of 2D shapes.	Make and draw shapes with increasing accuracy and apply knowledge of their properties	**Before:** Study a range of regular and irregular solid shapes. Discuss their properties; look at the shapes of their faces; point out which edge lengths are the same. **After:** Compare the shapes that the children have made. They should all be the same basic shape (a triangular prism with sloping faces at each end) but dimensions can vary.
B3		
Day out Solve practical division problems with remainders, in the context of organising a youth club visit to an adventure park.	Use knowledge of place value and multiplication facts to derive related division facts involving decimals	**Before:** Revise the different ways in which the remainder can be written after a division calculation – for example, as a fraction and as a decimal number. Discuss the different contexts that affect the decision to round the answer either up or down. **After:** Check the division method used by the children and the ways in which they have shown the remainder. Ask them to explain why they rounded the answer up or down. Can they think of other situations for rounding up or down? Which one seems to happen most frequently?
Best buy Carry out an investigation to find out whether it is more economical to buy three types of soft drink in large quantities.	• Tabulate systematically the information in a problem or puzzle; identify and record the steps or calculations needed to solve it, using symbols where appropriate; interpret solutions in the original context and check their accuracy • Use a calculator to solve problems involving multi-step calculations	**Before:** Discuss the nature of the problem with the children and show them examples of different drinks bottles with their prices. Stress that calculators will need to be used to get accurate results, but also that some rounding of numbers will be necessary. **After:** Answer the question: *Was it cheaper to buy the largest amount?* Discuss other factors in the buying process. Was the largest quantity actually needed?
Squares of multiples of 10 Identify squares of multiples of 10 up to 10,000.	Use knowledge of multiplication facts to derive quickly squares of numbers to 12 × 12 and the corresponding squares of multiples of 10	**Before:** Remind the children of the definition of square numbers and identify the square numbers up to 100. **After:** Collate all the squares of multiples of 10 up to 10,000.
Prime numbers up to 100 Colour all prime numbers up to 100 on a number square.	Recognise that prime numbers have only two factors and identify prime numbers less than 100	**Before:** Revise the definition of a prime number and show some examples. If there is time, talk about the fact that mathematicians are still looking for new prime numbers. **After:** Write all the prime numbers up to 100 on the board. Challenge the class to take part in the Mersenne project.
Properties of numbers Use rules of divisibility.	Use approximations, inverse operations and tests of divisibility to estimate and check results	**Before:** Revise the test of divisibility for 9. **After:** Test the rules with some examples given by the class.
Wedding madness! Use a calculator to calculate the cost of an extravagant wedding.	Use a calculator to solve problems involving multi-step calculations	**Before:** Talk about the techniques and strategies to adopt when using a calculator. Ensure that everyone has access to a calculator. **After:** Go over the answers with the class. Highlight any problems the children may have had reading and interpreting answers on the calculator screen.

Name	Date

Multiplying and dividing

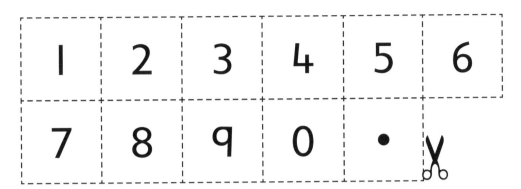

Instructions – a game for one player

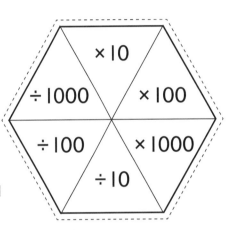

☐ Cut out the number and decimal point cards.

☐ Cut out the spinner and push a cocktail stick or used matchstick through the centre. You may wish to stick the spinner onto card to make it stronger.

☐ Turn the number cards face down. Pick three and arrange them to make a three-digit number (for example, 451).

☐ Spin the spinner and carry out the calculation it lands on. For example, with number cards 451 and the spinner on ÷100, the answer is 4·51.

☐ Fill in the chart on the right as you complete each calculation.

Challenge yourself! Try the game with four digits or include the decimal point card to generate a decimal number.

Number	Operation	Answer

BLOCK B

Dear Helper

This homework will help your child to reinforce the idea that when a number is multiplied by 10, the digits move one place to the left, two places when multiplied by 100 and three places for 1000. When dividing, the numbers move to the right. Encourage your child to complete at least six calculations and then check their answers. If correct, invite them to attempt the challenge, particularly the multiplication and division of decimals.

Name   Date

Name that shape

■ Read each clue and guess the mystery quadrilateral. You might want to sketch each shape to help you. There is more than one option for some answers.

1. I have one pair of parallel sides of different length. I have one pair of sides of equal length. What am I?

_____

2. I have no parallel sides. My adjacent sides are equal. My diagonals intersect at right angles. What am I?

_____

3. I have two pairs of parallel sides all of equal length. What am I?

_____

4. I have two pairs of parallel sides. My opposite sides are equal. I have two acute angles and two obtuse angles. What am I?

_____

5. All my sides are of equal length. I have two acute angles and two obtuse angles. What am I?

_____

6. I have one pair of parallel sides of different lengths. I have two right angles. What am I?

_____

Dear Helper
Your child will have done work on quadrilaterals in class. Some children will already know and remember the properties of quadrilaterals such as trapezium, rhombus, parallelogram and kite. Others may need to draw the shapes on a piece of paper so that they have a reference when working out each clue. Discuss the properties of each one before starting the homework.

Name	Date

What's next?

■ Look carefully at each sequence. For each one, write down the next three numbers or letters in the sequence and explain the rule.

1. 17 22 28 35 ⬜ ⬜ ⬜   The rule is _____

2. 98 50 26 ⬜ ⬜ ⬜   The rule is _____

3. 25 36 49 ⬜ ⬜ ⬜   The rule is _____

4. $\frac{1}{4}$ $\frac{2}{8}$ $\frac{4}{16}$ ⬜ ⬜ ⬜   The rule is _____

5. A D H ⬜ ⬜ ⬜   The rule is _____

6. 2 7 22 67 ⬜ ⬜ ⬜   The rule is _____

7. Now write three sequences of your own and explain the rule for each.

a) ⬜ ⬜ ⬜ ⬜ ⬜ ⬜ ⬜

  The rule is _____

b) ⬜ ⬜ ⬜ ⬜ ⬜ ⬜ ⬜

  The rule is _____

c) ⬜ ⬜ ⬜ ⬜ ⬜ ⬜ ⬜

  The rule is _____

Dear Helper
Point out to your child that sequences do not always increase with the same interval each time. For example, the pattern could be +2 +4 +6. Your child should also be encouraged to use multiplication in sequences, as well as addition and subtraction. Some sequences may have two operations in each step (for example, ×2 − 1). Encourage your child to look carefully at the difference between each number and use informal jottings to work out the pattern.

BLOCK B

Name   Date

What's it worth?

■ Work out the value of each bauble on the tree. The value of each letter is given below:

$a = 4$ $b = 3$ $c = 7$ $d = 5$ $e = 9$

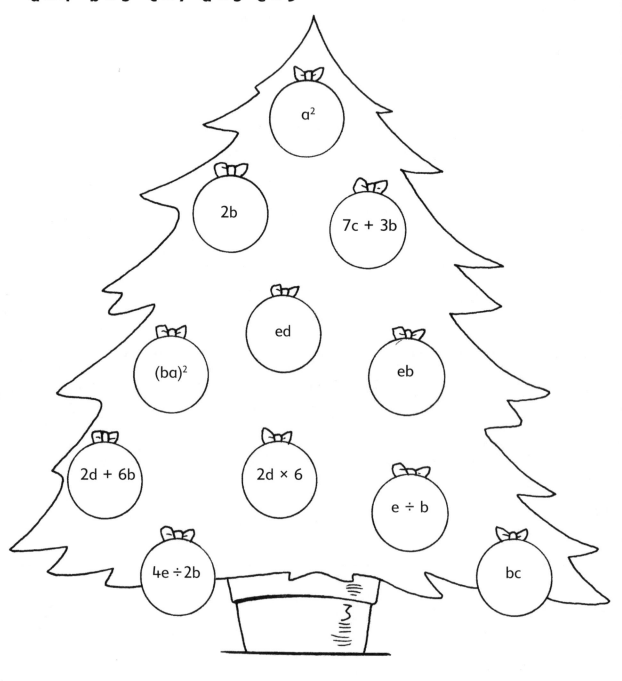

Baubles:
a^2
$2b$
$7c + 3b$
ed
$(ba)^2$
eb
$2d + 6b$
$2d \times 6$
$e \div b$
$4e \div 2b$
bc

Dear Helper
Remind the children that if a letter and number (or two letters) are next to each other, they must be multiplied, not added. Discuss also the meaning of the small 2 above a letter, which means 'squared' – multiplying a number by itself, not multiplying it by 2. Your child may be able to work out some answers mentally, but other numbers may need to be written down in an extended form before the answer can be calculated.

Name   Date

Fancy boxes

■ You will need some 1cm or 2cm square paper.

■ How many different nets can you draw for a cube? One has been drawn for you.

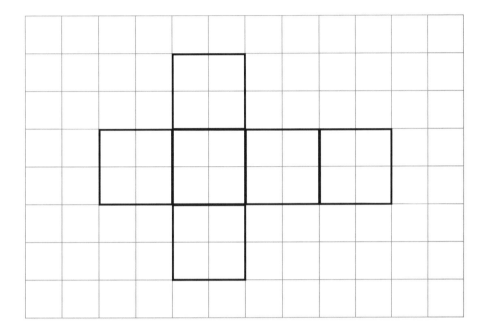

■ Draw the net for a cube on card and use it to make a box. Remember to add flaps so that you can stick the box together.

■ 'Choco' chocolate makers are looking for new designs for their latest product – 'Cruncho-choc'. Design and make some different-shaped boxes for 'Cruncho-choc'.

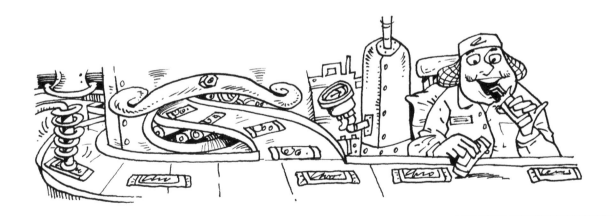

Dear Helper
Your child should know how to draw one net for a cube, but encourage them to draw as many different nets for a cube as they can. They could draw them on paper and cut them out to make sure that they do make a complete cube. For the second part of the activity, talk to your child about the different shapes they may use for the chocolate box, such as a square-based pyramid or a hexagonal prism. Find some examples of interesting boxes and help your child to work out what the nets will look like.

Name   Date

Floor shapes

■ Design a tile pattern for a floor using no more than four different tile shapes. These can be regular or irregular shapes as long as the pattern designed will tessellate.

Draw your shapes here.

Show how they will tessellate.

Dear Helper

The children have been learning about tile patterns and how shapes tessellate. Encourage your child to be imaginative but ensure that the shapes fit together exactly. It is useful to look at tile patterns in catalogues to help with ideas.

Name	Date

Boxed in

◼ Magic squares were first devised by the Chinese thousands of years ago. In a magic square each line (horizontally, vertically and diagonally) adds up to the same total. In the example shown right, the magic square total is 15.

4	9	2
3	5	7
8	1	6

Total = 15

◼ Complete the magic squares given below.

1.

10	35	
	25	
		40

3.

0.6		0.2
	0.5	
		0.4

2.

$\frac{1}{4}$		$\frac{1}{2}$
	$\frac{5}{8}$	
		1

4.

−2	3	2
	1	
		4

◼ In these number chains, complete the boxes by adding the previous two numbers. In the example shown, 3 + 4 = 7; 4 + 7 = 11 and 7 + 11 = 18.

3	4	7	11	18

5.

2		7	12	

6.

			15	24

7.

1				$12\frac{1}{2}$

Dear Helper

Go through the rules for magic squares and number chains with your child, as they will have to be followed correctly. Some revision of fractions and positive/negative numbers may also be needed. There is much potential in this type of activity and your child should be encouraged to create magic squares and number chains of their own for others to solve.

Name	Date

Euler's rule

- About 300 years ago, a famous mathematician called Leonhard Euler studied 3D shapes and discovered an important relationship.

  Euler's rule: In straight-sided 3D shapes, the number of edges equals the number of faces + the number of vertices (corners) – 2.

- Examine at least five straight-sided 3D shapes to prove this rule is true. Show your results in this table.

Shape	Number of vertices	Number of faces	Vertices + faces	Number of edges

- Examine some more straight-sided 3D shapes to see if this alternative version of the rule also works.

  Faces + vertices = edges + 2

Shape	Faces	Vertices	Edges + 2

Dear Helper
Your child will have done work on 3D shapes in class. Some will already know and remember the properties of common 3D shapes like cubes, cuboids and square-based pyramids. Others will need to have the shapes in front of them so that they can touch the parts physically. Discuss properties with them before starting to fill in the boxes. Ensure that only straight-sided 3D shapes are used to test out the rule as it will not fit shapes with curved edges like cylinders, cones and spheres.

Name	Date

Letter time

◼ If **m = 10, n = 12, p = 6 and q = 5,** find the values of the following statements.

1. $3q + 4 =$ _____

2. $m + 5p =$ _____

3. $12 + 3n =$ _____

4. $n - 2q =$ _____

5. $5q + m =$ _____

6. $\dfrac{pq}{m} =$ _____

7. $\dfrac{np}{6} =$ _____

8. $\dfrac{qn}{p} =$ _____

9. $p^2 - m - q =$ _____

10. $(4q + 3p) - n =$ _____

◼ Solve these number sentences.

11. $\triangle = 2\square + 1$ What is the value of $\triangle$ if:

$\square = 1$ _____ $\square = 3$ _____ $\square = 5$ _____

$\square = 2$ _____ $\square = 4$ _____

12. $2\triangle = \square + 2$ What is the value of $\triangle$ if:

$\square = 2$ _____ $\square = 6$ _____ $\square = 10$ _____

$\square = 4$ _____ $\square = 8$ _____

13. $\triangle = 3\square - 1$ What is the value of $\triangle$ if:

$\square = 1$ _____ $\square = 3$ _____ $\square = 5$ _____

$\square = 2$ _____ $\square = 4$ _____

14. $4\triangle = \square - 2$ What is the value of $\triangle$ if:

$\square = 2$ _____ $\square = 6$ _____ $\square = 10$ _____

$\square = 14$ _____

Dear Helper

Your child has been working on number puzzles in which letters and/or shapes are used as symbols to represent missing numbers. Remind them of several important rules before they start. Tell them to remember that 4 × m is usually written as 4m, and that where letters and numbers are written above others (for example, $\frac{45}{5}$), it means you should divide the number above the line by the number below the line. Challenge your child to make up some of their own number puzzles for others to solve.

Name   Date

 # Jumping frogs

- Imagine you own a jumping frog that only jumps in a regular pattern.

- Today he is jumping a small jump followed by a larger jump. He lands on the numbers 0, 2, 5, 7, 10 and 12.

1. What is the jumping rule? What are the next four numbers that your frog will land on?

_____

2. Sometimes your frog jumps differently. Find the rule and the next four numbers your frog will land on if it jumps in these sequences.

a) 0 ⟶ 4 ⟶ 7 ⟶ 11 ⟶ 14 _____

b) 0 ⟶ 6 ⟶ 9 ⟶ 15 ⟶ 18 _____

c) 0 ⟶ 7 ⟶ 12 ⟶ 19 ⟶ 24 _____

- Your frog can also jump backwards.

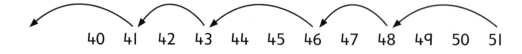

3. What is the number sequence now? What are the next four numbers?

_____

- Make up your own rules for jumping frogs. Try some out on the back of this sheet.

Dear Helper
Your child has experienced number patterns and sequences in class sessions. This is an extension of that work except that the sequences on this activity sheet all follow a two-step rule rather than one-step. Encourage your child to work from the known to the unknown (ie working out what the rule is and then using it to predict what numbers will follow as the sequence continues). Some children prefer to write down what is happening to the sequence in each gap. Their own variations can be almost endless.

BLOCK B

Name	Date

How old are they?

■ Study these facts to answer the questions.

☐ In six years Ann will be the age that her brother Ben is now.

☐ Ben is 12 years old.

☐ Their mother is six times Ann's age and is three years younger than her husband.

1. How old is Ann?...

2. How old is Ann's father?...

3. How old was Ann's mother when Ann was born?..................................

4. How old was Ann's father when Ben was born?...................................

5. How old was Ben when Ann was two?..

6. When Ann's father is 60, how old will her mother be? ....

7. In how many years will Ann's mother be exactly $2\frac{1}{2}$ times

as old as Ben?...

8. How old will Ann's father be when Ben is 21?.....................................

■ Think of some more questions you could ask about the ages of Ann's family.

Dear Helper
This is a puzzle to complete together. Remind your child about the facts that you have been given.
Make sure they realise that the family all age, so next year they will all be one year older. Think of some
other questions you could ask each other related to the problem.

BLOCK B

BLOCK B

Name   Date

Build it

◼ You will need some thin card.

◼ Sketch a 3D shape that you could make using:

☐ 2 trapeziums

☐ 2 triangles

☐ 1 rectangle

Sketch your shape here.

◼ Make your shape using thin card. Think carefully about the measurements for your 2D shapes, to ensure they join together correctly to make a 3D shape. Which edges need to be the same length?

◼ Remember to add tabs to your 2D shapes so that you can join them to make the 3D shape.

Dear Helper

Your child has been learning to visualise 3D shapes. If your child finds this visualisation difficult, it may be helpful to cut out some 2D shapes and experiment with them first.

Name   Date

Day out

- Elm Tree youth club is going on a day out to the local adventure park. During the day the organisers face some tricky division problems.

- Solve each of the problems for them, giving at least two different ways of showing the remainder. For each answer you will have to round up or round down, depending on the situation.

1. Four adults and 32 children are going on the visit. The minibuses the organisers can hire hold 14 passengers each. How many minibuses are needed?

2. The total cost of entrance tickets is £204. Everyone has paid in £10 notes. How many notes do you need to hand over?

3. A kind adult helper decides to share out one hundred sweets equally among the children only. How many sweets will they each have?

4. The party visits the Butterfly House. Visitors must go round in groups of ten. How many groups will the youth club party make?

5. To make sure that no one gets thirsty on the trip, another of the helpers thinks they need 24 litres of bottled water for the day. Water comes in five-litre bottles. How many bottles does she need to buy?

6. Sanjay, one of the children, has £2 to spend on souvenirs. He likes the animal badges that are 35p each. How many can he buy?

Dear Helper
These practical division problems will each leave a remainder and each situation requires the answer to be rounded up or down to the nearest whole number. Encourage your child to write down the calculation and show how they worked it out. They should also discuss the problem and be prepared to give their reasoning about the rounding up or down procedure. Get them to read the question carefully and apply common sense to the answer.

Name   Date

Best buy

- ◼ You will need to use a calculator for this task.

- ◼ You are going to investigate if it is cheaper to buy items in large quantities.

- ◼ In the table below is the capacity of three types of bottle, containing orange, lemonade and water. Prices are also given.

- ◼ Work out which bottle of each drink provides the best value for money. Calculate how much 100ml of each drink costs by dividing the cost of the 500ml bottle by 5, the one-litre bottle by 10 and the two-litre bottle by 20. Round off each answer to the nearest penny. The first one has been done for you.

Drink	Capacity	Price	Cost per 100ml
Orange	500ml	£0.69	£0.69 ÷ 5 = £0.138 = £0.14
	one litre	£1.15	
	two litre	£1.29	
Lemonade	500ml	£0.29	
	one litre	£0.39	
	two litre	£0.55	
Water	500ml	£0.39	
	one litre	£0.59	
	two litre	£0.75	

- ◼ Is it cheaper to buy the largest capacity bottle? Is this always the case?

- ◼ Collect a range of plastic drinks bottles of differing capacities at home and carry out further pricing research.

Dear Helper

This is a practical problem that shoppers are faced with frequently. Your child will need to work with the quantities hand prices provided on the sheet using a calculator. As an extension, they should carry out their own research. Provide labelled drinks bottles and details of how much each of them costs. Analyse the results with your child. Look at other factors in the buying process. Was the largest capacity actually needed? What would happen if it was not used up straight away? Does the higher cost of the larger capacity bottles put some customers off?

PHOTOCOPIABLE 📖SCHOLASTIC

Name	Date

Squares of multiples of 10

◀ How many squares of multiples of 10 lie between 2000 and 5000?

◀ Write as many as you can in this box. One has been done for you.

$50 \times 50 = 2500$

◀ How many squares of multiples of 10 lie between 1000 and 10,000?

◀ Write as many as you can in this box. One has been done for you.

$70 \times 70 = 4900$

BLOCK B

Dear Helper
This activity will help your child to understand the value of learning multiplication facts and also show them how these facts can be used to good effect. Your child may need reminding that when a number is squared it is multiplied by itself.

Name	Date

Prime numbers up to 100

🔲 A prime number is a number greater than 1 that only has two factors: itself and 1. Prime numbers are always odd (apart from the number 2!).

🔲 Your challenge is to identify all the prime numbers up to 100.

🔲 Colour them in on this 100-square.

1	2	3	4	5	6	7	8	9	10
11	12	13	14	15	16	17	18	18	20
21	22	23	24	25	26	27	28	29	30
31	32	33	34	35	36	37	38	39	40
41	42	43	44	45	46	47	48	49	50
51	52	53	54	55	56	57	58	59	60
61	62	63	64	65	66	67	68	69	70
71	72	73	74	75	76	77	78	79	80
81	82	83	84	85	86	87	88	89	90
91	92	93	94	95	96	97	98	99	100

Dear Helper

This activity will help your child to remember prime numbers. They could use the method called the Sieve of Eratosthenes (created by the ancient Greek mathematician, Eratosthenes!): cross out all multiples of 2, then all multiples of 3 (and so on), up to multiples of 10. The numbers not crossed out are prime numbers. Once your child has completed this activity, you could challenge them to find the next 20 prime numbers after 100. There is a substantial international prize available if anyone can find a prime number with over 10 million digits. That should keep them busy for a while!

PHOTOCOPIABLE 📖SCHOLASTIC

BLOCK B

Name	Date

Properties of numbers

◀ A whole number can be divided by:

▢ 3 if the sum of the digits is divisible by 3

▢ 6 if it is even and is also divisible by 3

▢ 8 if half of it is divisible by 4

▢ 9 if the sum of the digits is divisible by 9

◀ Circle the numbers in each set that can be divided exactly by 8.

1. 9   16   18   32   38   40

2. 6   22   35   48   53   62

3. 64   79   82   88   98   100

◀ Circle the numbers in each set that can be divided exactly by 6.

4. 14   18   22   25   30   38

5. 12   19   24   31   36   44

6. 42   49   54   62   70   72

◀ Circle the numbers in each set that can be divided exactly by 3.

7. 12   14   21   25   28   33

8. 21   29   34   36   40   48

9. 62   75   79   84   87   93

◀ Circle the numbers in each set that can be divided exactly by 9.

10. 26   38   45   54   68   72

11. 105   108   144   158   172   190

12. 426   532   702   833   920   9783

Dear Helper

This activity will help your child to remember the divisibility tests for 3, 6, 8 and 9. These rules and tips are very useful to learn. Once your child has mastered them, experiment with much larger numbers on the back of this sheet.

Name   Date

Wedding madness!

■ Footballer Gary Goalie is marrying Mystique from the pop group Flirty Foxes.

■ Use a calculator to work out the total cost of their wedding.

■ There will be 483 guests at the wedding.

- ☐ A seven-course meal: £52 per head
- ☐ 1200 bottles of champagne: £33 each
- ☐ The band will play for 3½ hours: £3250 per hour
- ☐ 127 flower arrangements: £27.50 each
- ☐ A goody bag for each guest: £175 per bag
- ☐ 212 taxis: £17 each

Total cost = ☐

■ However, Gary plays for lowly Dumpton Town and gets paid £200 per week.
How many weeks will it take Gary to pay for the wedding? ☐

Dear Helper

This activity will help your child to become more confident using a calculator. When using a calculator, it is always worth double-checking the answers as it only takes a few seconds. It is very easy for children to press the keys and just assume that what they see on the screen is correct. Make sure that your child gets into the habit of checking their answers.

Handling data and measures

Activity name	Learning objectives	Managing the homework
C1		
What's on? Use a TV guide to produce a grouped data bar chart.	Construct and interpret frequency tables and bar charts with grouped data	**Before:** Revise the term 'grouped data'. Discuss the most suitable units to use on the y axis. **After:** Ask: *What was the most frequent (mode) length of programme? Which channel had the most programmes lasting over 1½ hours?* Ask more questions to ensure that the children can interpret their graph.
A good guess Estimate weights of a range of objects and check estimates using scales.	● Use standard metric units of measure and convert between units using decimals to two places (for example, change 2.75 litres to 2750ml) ● Read and interpret scales on a range of measuring instruments, recording results to a required degree of accuracy	**Before:** Revise how to write measurements in different ways (for example, 250g = 0.25kg = 0kg 250g). **After:** Discuss how successful children were with their estimations. Was there a particular weight (for example, 1kg) that they could use as a benchmark for estimating other weights?
My day On a pie chart, plot how a day (24 hours) is spent and show the activities as percentages of the whole.	Construct and interpret pie charts	**Before:** Discuss how to calculate the angle for each activity. Remind the children that there are 360 degrees at the centre of the circle. **After:** Ask the children to explain how they calculated percentages related to their pie charts.
Dicey Dave Test a statement by conducting a fair test and draw a bar chart from data gathered in a tally chart.	● Collect, organise and represent information, interpret results and review methods; identify and answer related questions ● Construct and interpret frequency tables and bar charts	**Before:** Discuss what constitutes a fair test. Ensure that all children have access to at least one dice so that they can carry out the activity at home. **After:** Compare class results. Collate class information and display it in graph form.
C2		
What's the chance? Plot a series of statements on a probability scale.	Describe and predict outcomes from data using the language of chance or likelihood	**Before:** Revise the probability scale 0-1 and the language of probability. **After:** Draw a probability scale on the board. Ask the children where they placed the various statements.
Make a guess Carry out measurement tasks at home, estimating first. Record the measurements in at least two different ways.	● Use standard metric units of measure and convert between units using decimals to two places (for example, change 2.75 litres to 2750ml) ● Read and interpret scales on a range of measuring instruments, recognising that the measurement is approximate and recording results to a required degree of accuracy	**Before:** Talk about choosing the right piece of equipment for the measuring task being considered. Discuss methods of estimation. Revise converting measurements into smaller or larger units. **After:** Discuss a sample of children's results. How close were estimations? Did estimations improve with practice? Which measuring device was the easiest to use?
How many koruna? Draw a currency conversion graph and then solve simple conversion problems using the graph.	Construct and interpret line graphs	**Before:** Remind the children that they only need to plot one exchange value and draw the straight line graph from zero. They must think carefully about the scale. Discuss the different currencies used in Europe (the euro is used in many parts, but there are still other currencies). **After:** Check that the children solved the problems using the graph. Ask them to demonstrate how they were able to use a calculator to check their answers.

Handling data and measures

Activity name	Learning objectives	Managing the homework
Island Paradisio temperatures Find the mode, median, mean and range of temperatures.	Describe and interpret results and solutions to problems using the mode, range, median and mean	**Before:** Recap on the definitions of mode, range, median and mean. Remind the children how to calculate the mean of a group of numbers. **After:** Discuss the answers and compare results.
C3		
In a spin Investigate the probability of landing on numbers on a spinning device.	Describe and predict outcomes from data using the language of chance or likelihood	**Before:** Revise the probability scale 0–1 and language of probability. **After:** Did the children's predictions match the outcomes?
Book your own break Plan a weekend break and calculate costs.	Solve problems by collecting, selecting, processing, presenting and interpreting data, using ICT where appropriate; draw conclusions and identify further questions to ask	**Before:** Ensure that the children know where to look for the information they will need to complete the activity (holiday brochures and the internet). **After:** Compare different styles of holiday brochure. Discuss how information is presented and what to look for in the 'small print'.
Ferry crossing Calculate the cost of different ferry routes; refer to tables similar to those in ferry brochures.	Solve problems by selecting and processing data; draw conclusions and identify further questions to ask	**Before:** Ensure that the children understand how important it is to read all the information given to them before they start trying to answer the questions. **After:** Discuss any common errors. Check that all the children understand that the prices are for single journeys, and that they took account of the ages of the children in the family.
Island Paradisio rainfall Analyse the range and mean of a set of rainfall data. Present a set of data with a given mode.	Describe and interpret results and solutions to problems using the mode, range and mean	**Before:** Recap on the 'Island Paradisio temperatures' activity (page 50). **After:** Ensure that all the children are solid with their understanding of the mode, range, median and mean.

BLOCK C

Name	Date

What's on?

◀ Use a page from a TV-listings magazine or the TV page from a newspaper to find out how many programmes of different length are shown on BBC 1, BBC 2 and ITV.

◀ Choose a day to investigate, starting at 9am and finishing at 9pm.

◀ Use these tally charts to record the length of each programme.

BBC 1	5–15 minutes	16–30 minutes	31–45 minutes	46–60 minutes	61–75 minutes	76–90 minutes	Over 91 minutes

BBC 2	5–15 minutes	16–30 minutes	31–45 minutes	46–60 minutes	61–75 minutes	76–90 minutes	Over 91 minutes

ITV	5–15 minutes	16–30 minutes	31–45 minutes	46–60 minutes	61–75 minutes	76–90 minutes	Over 91 minutes

◀ Use the information to produce a grouped data bar chart on the back of this sheet. Use a different colour for each channel (see example below).

◀ You will need to decide upon what intervals to use on the y axis. Don't forget: a title; to label each axis; to draw a key to show which is each channel.

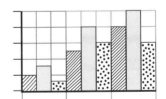

◀ Now answer the following questions:

1. What is the most frequent length of TV programme?

2. Which channel has the most programmes over 90 minutes?

3. Which channel has the most programmes under 30 minutes?

4. Which channel has the most programmes that last 45–60 minutes?

Dear Helper

Any TV listing schedule can be used for this homework, whether it be a page from a newspaper or a page from a TV magazine. Work alongside your child to produce the tally chart. Discuss suitable intervals for the y axis, dependent upon the numbers generated in each section. Ask your child each of the four questions to check their interpretation of the graph.

BLOCK C

Name		Date	

A good guess

■ You will need a pair of kitchen scales and various objects to weigh – for example, a book, an apple, a pencil case, or a mug. Make sure you ask permission before using anything!

■ First estimate the weight of each object.

■ Weigh each object to see how accurate your estimate was.

■ Record your information in the chart below, writing the weights in three different ways. Remember: 1250g = 1.25kg = 1kg 250g.

Object	Estimate	Actual weight		
		g	**kg**	**kg and g**

Dear Helper
Provide a range of objects that will give quite different weights. Make sure that your child knows how to read your scales, as they may be quite different to the ones used in school. Check that they write each measurement correctly in three different ways, such as 630g = 0·63kg = 0kg 630g.

Name	Date

My day

■ You are going to draw a pie chart to show how you spend your time in a typical day at the weekend.

■ Think about how you spend your day (24 hours) and put the information into this chart (for example, sleeping = 8 hours and 30 minutes). Round up or down to the nearest 30 minutes. If necessary, use an extra sheet of paper for recording and working out.

Activity	Hours and minutes

■ Draw a pie chart to show proportionately how your time is spent.

■ Write the percentage of the day spent doing each activity in the relevant section.

Dear Helper
This activity is designed to develop your child's understanding of pie charts and percentages. Discuss how a period of 24 hours is spent. Your child must then calculate what percentage of the 24 hours is spent on each of the activities.

Name   Date

Dicey Dave

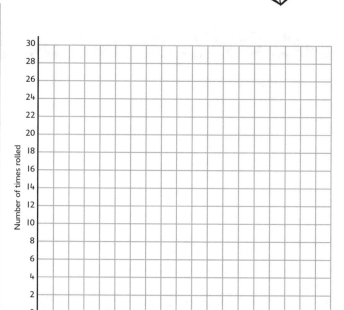

- Dicey Dave says the total that is most common when three dice are rolled is 9.

- Put Dicey Dave's theory to the test!

- Roll three dice 100 times and record the results in this tally chart.

Dice total	Tally	Frequency
3		
4		
5		
6		
7		
8		
9		
10		
11		
12		
13		
14		
15		
16		
17		
18		

- Use the information to present your results as a bar chart on the back of this sheet (see example above).

1. Do you think Dicey Dave was correct?

_____

2. Which total (or totals) were rolled the most?

_____

3. Which total (or totals) were rolled the least?

_____

4. Why did these totals appear the least/most?

_____

Dear Helper

This activity will help your child to understand that different events have different probabilities. It is helpful if you do have three dice (look in board games and remember to put them back!) but you could use one dice and roll it three times for each tally. Question the results with your child. Did they conduct a fair test?

BLOCK C

Name   Date

What's the chance?

◼ Read each of these statements.

◼ Decide the likelihood of each event.

◼ Draw a line from each statement to the correct place on the probability scale.

| You will see Queen Victoria walking down the road today. |

| It will rain tomorrow. |

| Your headteacher will close the school tomorrow. |

| You will watch TV tonight. |

| You will have toast for breakfast next Thursday. |

| The sun will rise tomorrow. |

| Christmas Day will be on the 25th December. |

| You will go to the moon next Tuesday. |

| You will sneeze this evening. |

1

0

BLOCK C

Dear Helper
Probability is an area of maths used in many real-life situations, ranging from lottery forecasts to weather predictions. Discuss the likelihood of each event and ask your child to explain why they have chosen each position on the probability scale. Encourage your child to generate their own questions to put on the scale.

Name   Date

Make a guess

◾ You will need a 30cm ruler, a metre stick (or equivalent strip of paper) and a measuring tape to carry out this task.

◾ You are going to carry out some measurement tasks at home using each of these three pieces of measuring equipment. Choose items suitable for the type of measuring device you are using (for example, a book for the ruler, a shelf for the metre stick and the length of a room for the tape measure). Aim to measure ten items with each device.

◾ Before you measure each item, estimate how long you think it will be and write down your estimate. When measuring each item, be accurate to the nearest millimetre. If this proves difficult, round to the nearest half-centimetre.

◾ Finally, write down the measurements in at least one other way (for example, 7cm 8mm could be written as 78mm, 94cm could be written as 0.94m and 5m 17cm could be written as 517cm).

◾ Draw a table like this on the back of the sheet to record your answers.

Item measured	Estimate	Measurement	Second recording

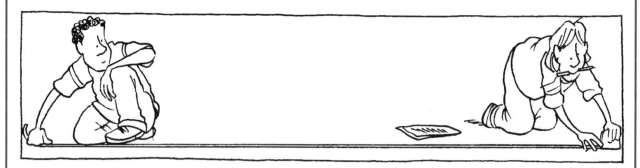

Dear Helper
Three important aspects of length measurements are featured in this task. Your child will be able to practise estimation, work with several different types of measuring device and learn to write the same length measurements in a number of different ways. Please help them to find the equipment they need and suitable, safe items to measure before starting. Afterwards discuss whether their estimations improved with practice. Which of the measuring devices was the easiest to use? Talk about practical measuring tasks that you have to carry out at home.

Name   Date

How many koruna?

■ The Rashid family are going to Prague for the weekend. They will change their money before they go and expect to get 39.34 koruna to the pound.

■ When they are there they want to be able to work out the cost of items so they would like to take a conversion graph with them.

■ Draw a conversion graph for pound sterling to koruna.

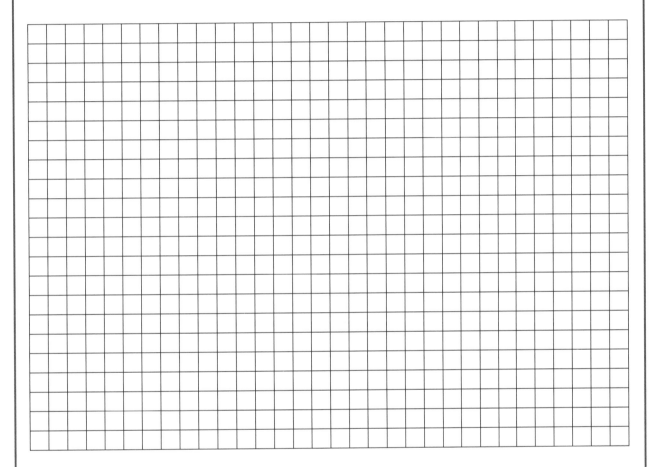

1. Their restaurant bill is 1288 koruna.
Use your graph to find out how much that is in sterling. _____

2. Ali wants to change the pocket money he has saved.
How many koruna will he get for £15.50? _____

Dear Helper
Your child has been learning how to draw conversion graphs. In this activity they are asked to draw a graph to convert Czech Republic koruna to sterling and vice versa. They should draw a graph for a range of 0 to 100 pounds sterling. Make sure that they label the axes carefully, ensuring that the intervals between the values are regular. You may like to test them with some sample exchanges; these can be checked using a calculator. Your child may like to draw some extra conversion graphs, such as koruna to euros, or sterling to other currencies.

Name   Date

Island Paradisio temperatures

■ These are the temperatures (in °C) for a two-week period on the holiday island Paradisio.

Week 1	Week 2
25, 26, 26, 23, 24, 30, 28	28, 28, 32, 28, 33, 35, 26

1. What was the mode temperature for week 1? _____

2. What was the range of temperatures for week 1? _____

3. What was the median temperature for week 1? _____

4. What was the mean temperature for week 1? _____

5. Now work out the same for week 2:

Mode temperature: _____   Range of temperatures: _____

Median temperature: _____   Mean temperature: _____

6. What were the mode, median and mean temperatures and range of temperatures

on Paradisio for the two-week period? _____

Dear Helper
This activity will help children to remember how to calculate different averages. The mean is the average of a group of numbers. You add all the numbers and divide by the number of amounts. The median is the middle value in a group of numbers and the mode is the most common value in a group of numbers. The range is the difference between the greatest and the least in a set of numbers.

BLOCK C

Name	Date

In a spin

■ Cut out the spinner below. Push a cocktail stick or a used matchstick through the centre so that it will spin easily. You might want to stick the spinner onto card to make it stronger.

■ Look at the spinner and answer these questions:

1. What is the chance of landing on a 5?

_____

2. What is the chance of landing on an even number?

_____

3. What is the chance of landing on an odd number?

_____

■ Spin the spinner eight times – record each number as you land on it. How similar were your outcomes to the answers you recorded above?

■ Do two more sets of eight spins. Compare the results.

■ How accurate do you think the rules of probability are?

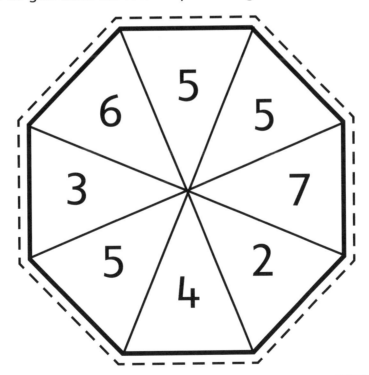

Dear Helper

Ask your child some questions before they begin to find out which numbers they think the spinner is most/least likely to land on, and why. Their first set of eight spins may not tie in particularly well with their answers to the questions but the more spins they do, the more closely their results should reflect the actual probability of each outcome.

Name   Date

Book your own break

- Plan a weekend break to somewhere in Europe.

- First you will need to research your chosen destination, using the internet and brochures collected from your local travel agent.

- Think about the following:

  ◻ What weather can you expect?

  ◻ How much will the flights cost for you and your family?

  ◻ How much will the accommodation cost?

  ◻ How much spending money will you need?

- Remember that when you choose your flights you must ask:

  ◻ Are the flights one-way or return?

  ◻ Are there additional costs such as airport taxes?

  > Record your choice of destination and holiday costs here.

Dear Helper
This activity is designed to help your child investigate the costs involved with planning a holiday. They can use the internet to search for prices and also use holiday brochures from a travel agent. Encourage your child to look at different holiday options and to justify their choices.

Name	Date

Ferry crossing

Month	Car plus two passengers	Motorcycle plus rider	Adult foot passenger	Child foot passenger
January	99	49	22	11
February	99	49	22	11
March	99	49	22	11
April	130	65	25	15
May	130	65	25	15
June	130	65	25	15
July	150	70	30	18
August	150	70	30	18
September	130	65	25	15
October	100	49	22	11
November	100	49	22	11
December	100	49	22	11
Prices for a single crossing				
Additional adults in a car £5 All children under 15yrs in a car travel free				
Mini-break – up to five days abroad 40% discount				
Saver – up to ten days abroad 20% discount				

1. How much does it cost for a family of two adults and three children under 15, travelling by car, for a two-week trip, leaving in August and returning in September?

_____

2. Calculate the cost for a mini-break of four days in May for four adults in a car.

_____

3. How much does it cost for two adults to take their car for eight days in October?

_____

4. What will the fare be for two adults and three children without a car, travelling for two weeks in June?

_____

Dear Helper

This activity is designed to help your child learn to extract information from tables. Encourage them to read all the information carefully, especially the 'small print'. You may like to make up some questions of your own related to the information, such as costs for your own family to travel.

Name

Date

Island Paradisio rainfall

■ This bar chart shows the amount of rainfall on the holiday island Paradisio.

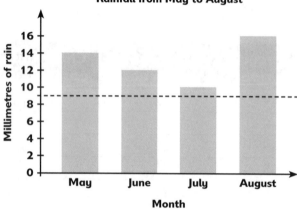

Rainfall from May to August

■ Justine says: *The dotted line on the chart shows the mean rainfall for the four months.*

1. Use the chart to explain why Justine cannot be correct.

Justine is incorrect because _____

_____

_____

2. What is the mean rainfall on Island Paradisio for the four months? _____

3. Give different values for the monthly rainfall totals but keep the mean the same.

_____

4. What is the range of rainfall in these four months? _____

5. Write a number in each of these boxes so that the mode of the five numbers is 11.

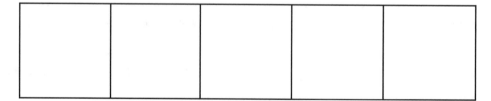

Dear Helper

This activity will help your child to develop a better understanding of different averages. Encourage your child to look at the information very carefully and understand what they are being asked to do. Do they know the meaning of the words *mean*, *mode* and *range*? If not, they can look them up in a dictionary or online.

Calculating, measuring and understanding shape

Activity name	Learning objectives	Managing the homework
D1		
Use your loaf Children calculate how many slices of bread they eat in a year.	Solve multi-step problems; choose and use appropriate calculation strategies at each stage, including calculator use	**Before:** Ensure that the children know there are 52 weeks or 365 days in a year. Discuss that the answer will only be approximate. As a starting point, how many slices of bread do they eat in a week? **After:** Discuss the range of answers and ask the children to share some of their methods.
Mr Fixit Work out the different perimeters of shapes with the same area.	Calculate the perimeter and area of rectilinear shapes; estimate the area of an irregular shape by counting squares	**Before:** Explain that for the second activity, the patio tiles must fit together side by side. They cannot overlap, or join together with just the corners touching. **After:** Ask the children for the different perimeters found. *Which would be the best arrangement for a patio?* Ask them to share their own compound shapes. *Which had the biggest perimeter?*
Give me room! Calculate the floor space of a number of rooms to see which one has the largest area. Find the perimeter of the rooms as an extension activity.	Calculate the perimeter and area of rectilinear shapes	**Before:** Ask: *What is the formula for finding the area of a rectangle?* (length × width) Revise the fact that compound shapes have to be split into convenient rectangles to make the calculation of the floor area easier. **After:** Make sure that the children are agreed on which room has the biggest floor area. Check perimeter solutions and discuss methods. Investigate examples of room sizes taken from home.
Supermarket shopping Use a supermarket shopping bill to calculate the cost of various items.	Use efficient written methods to add and subtract integers and decimals, and to multiply and divide integers and decimals by a one-digit integer	**Before:** Talk to the children about how supermarket bills are presented. They will have to find the items mentioned in the questions and then perform various calculations to determine the answers. **After:** Go through the answers with the class. How many children missed out items when asked to price the fruit? Were there any other omissions?
D2		
Picture this Plot a picture on a grid and write down the coordinates only. Helper tries to draw the picture on the grid.	Use coordinates to draw and locate shapes	**Before:** Discuss how to write coordinates correctly. Explain that each coordinate must be written in order so that their partner can join up each point to create a picture. **After:** How successful were the children in (a) creating their own coordinate pictures and (b) providing accurate coordinates for their helper? Choose a grid from one of the children and ask the rest of the class to draw the picture on their grid.
In a word Solve eight word-based problems taken from real-life situations. The first four problems involve single step operations; the second four require multistep operations.	Solve multi-step problems and problems involving decimals; choose and use appropriate calculation strategies at each stage, including calculator use	**Before:** Revise problem-solving strategies. Stress key points like picking out vital information and choosing the best operation. Decisions will also have to be made about how calculations should be carried out – for example, mental, mental with jottings or formal written methods. **After:** Check answers and review the strategies and methods that the children have used. What methods were used to estimate and approximate answers initially. Did answers make sense? How were solutions checked?

BLOCK D

Calculating, measuring and understanding shape

Activity name	Learning objectives	Managing the homework
How big is the angle? Estimate the size of an angle and then measure it accurately.	Estimate angles, and use a protractor to measure and draw them on their own	**Before:** Make sure that each child has a protractor. Remind them that the protractor must be positioned correctly and to check the direction of the scale. Ensure that they recognise a right angle as 90° and can use this to estimate the size of other angles. **After:** Discuss any difficulties. Ask the children if their estimating skills improved as they worked through the exercise.
Battleships Plot and locate grid references to find the position of battleships.	Use coordinates to draw and locate shapes	**Before:** Remind the children about the four quadrants and how grid references are given; first the x axis and then the y axis. **After:** Look at any answers that the children are disputing. Ask them to give you the coordinates of some of their battleships and let other children plot them on the board.
D3		
Dream playground Design a dream playground and calculate the areas of different parts.	Calculate the perimeter and area of rectilinear shapes; estimate the area of an irregular shape by counting squares	**Before:** The children may need squared paper and should understand about drawing a plan to a simple scale. They will need to be able to calculate areas of simple compound shapes. **After:** Invite the children to discuss and compare their designs within a small group. Check that they have used the scale correctly and that the areas have been calculated correctly.
Entertainment! Calculate the costs for two different options for a birthday treat.	Solve multi-step problems and problems involving decimals; choose and use appropriate calculation strategies at each stage, including calculator use	**Before:** Remind the children that they should approximate their answer first. Encourage them to think about which option they think will be the cheaper. **After:** Check that the children have included the cost for Mark. What method did they use to check the accuracy of their answer?
Bedroom furniture Choose and plan the furniture for a dream bedroom. Draw a scale plan and calculate costs.	Solve multi-step problems and problems involving decimals; choose and use appropriate calculation strategies at each stage, including calculator use	**Before:** Ensure that the children have access to catalogues or brochures for furniture. Tell them to look carefully at prices; are there any special offers or discounts? Remind them about scale drawing and discuss how much space is needed for each piece of furniture. **After:** Ask the children to compare their plans and the cost of furniture. As a group they should choose suitable items and agree one choice of layout.
Carpet fitter Calculate the costs involved in fitting a carpet.	Solve multi-step problems and problems involving decimals; choose and use appropriate calculation strategies at each stage, including calculator use	**Before:** Explain to the children that carpet comes in rolls and although it is often priced by the square metre, when it is cut from the roll the customer must pay for the full width, so there is often wasted carpet. **After:** Ask the children to explain how they reached a solution. Check that they have included the cost of underlay.

BLOCK D

SCHOLASTIC

Name	Date

Use your loaf

◀ How many slices of bread do you eat in a year? 400? 500? More? Less? Now is your chance to find out!

◀ First of all, write an estimate here: _____ slices of bread.

◀ What calculation strategies could help you? What will you need to do first? Use the box below to write down some ideas.

◀ Choose the method you think will work best and use the box below to complete your calculations.

◀ How many slices do you eat? Is it more or less than you estimated?

_____

◀ I eat _____ slices of bread in a year.

Dear Helper
Help your child to estimate how many slices of bread they eat in a week and, from that, a whole year. Discuss ways in which you could estimate such an amount. The children have learned a range of methods for multiplying. Tell them to choose the one they feel most comfortable with, and ask them to explain the process. Encourage them to check their answer by using another method of multiplying or by using the inverse operation (division).

BLOCK D

Name   Date

Mr Fixit

◼ Mr Fixit has to build a new patio in the garden of The Crossed Forks restaurant. He has 60 one metre square patio slabs. What different rectangular patios can he make with his slabs? Which arrangement gives the greatest perimeter? Record your findings in this chart.

Length	Width	Perimeter

◼ The restaurant owners have decided not to have a rectangular patio. Use either the grid below or a separate sheet of squared paper to find the compound shape that will give the greatest perimeter. The patio slabs must fit together side by side – they cannot overlap or join together with just the corners touching. What is the biggest perimeter you can find?

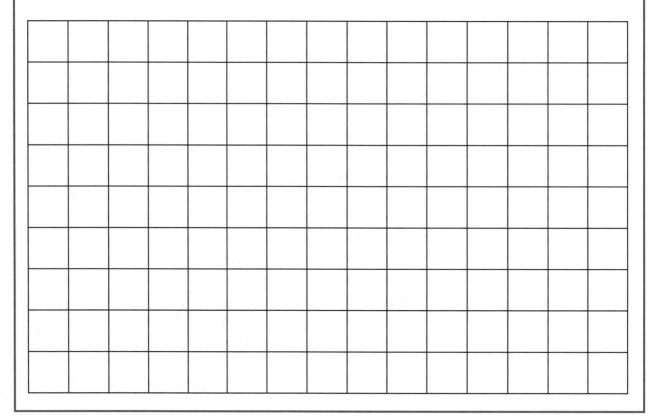

BLOCK D

Dear Helper
Check that your child understands that perimeter means the distance around the edge of a shape. Encourage them to draw each rectangle on squared paper. Discuss efficient ways of finding perimeter, rather than counting each square. For instance, adding together the width and length, and multiplying by 2.

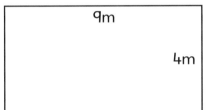
Name	Date

Give me room!

◼ The Johnson family is moving house. Sarah Johnson has been looking at details of some of the houses they have been to see because she wants to have the largest bedroom possible.

◼ The measurements of the rooms she has seen so far are given below. Work out the floor area of each one to find out which will provide most space.

Room 1

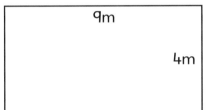

9m

4m

Room 2

$3\frac{1}{2}$ m

12m

Room 3

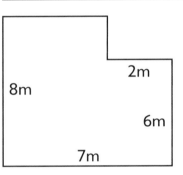

2m

8m

6m

7m

Room 4

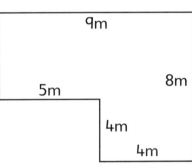

9m

8m

5m

4m

4m

Room 5

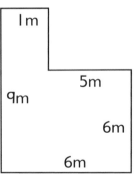

1m

5m

9m

6m

6m

Room 6

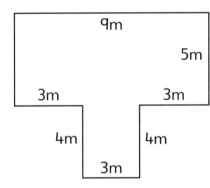

9m

5m

3m

3m

4m

4m

3m

◼ As an extension activity, calculate what the perimeter of each room will be.

◼ Work with your helper to find the floor area of some of the bedrooms at home. Record the results on the back of this sheet.

Dear Helper

Before starting, ensure that your child understands the difference between area and perimeter. Stress the fact that compound shapes should be split up into convenient rectangles to make the calculation easier. When measuring rooms at home to find their floor area, some measurements may need to be rounded off, or a calculator used, to carry out calculations.

BLOCK D

Name   Date

Supermarket shopping

🔲 This is Harry's shopping bill.

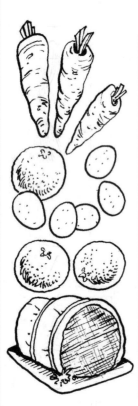

SUPERMARKET

Free-range eggs × 6.............................1.32
Carrots 250g......................................0.45
Oranges × 12.....................................1.98
King Edward potatoes 2.5kg................1.75
Yoghurt × 4.......................................0.88
Kiwi fruits × 5....................................1.20
Granny Smith apples 500g..................0.75
Seedless grapes 200g.........................0.65
Coffee 100g.......................................1.95
Tea bags × 200..................................1.99
Semi-skimmed milk 2l........................1.60
Topside beef 1.5kg.............................7.50

1. How much did Harry spend on fruit altogether? _____

2. How much is one free-range egg? _____

3. What is the price per kg of carrots? _____

4. How much per kg are King Edward potatoes? _____

5. How much are yoghurts each? _____

6. How much is one kiwi fruit? _____

7. How much are grapes per kg? _____

8. How much did Harry spend altogether? _____

Dear Helper

This activity gives your child practice in using decimals in calculations. Encourage your child to try calculating mentally at first. When adding up, make sure that they put the decimal points in line. Remind them to think about whether their answer is reasonable or not. Have a look at some of your own supermarket bills and make up some questions about your shopping.

Name	Date

Picture this

🔲 Design a coordinate picture for a friend (or adult helper) to try.

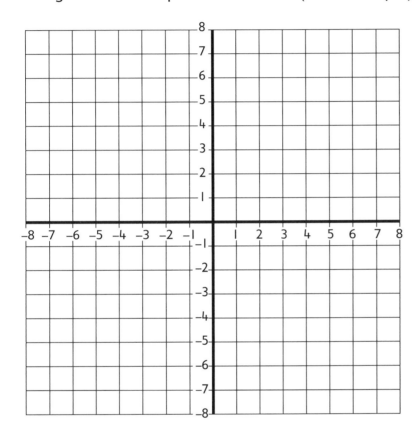

🔲 Use the grid above to plan your design. Your design must go into all four quadrants.

🔲 Write down the coordinates of your design and give them to your partner to copy onto a blank coordinate grid.

🔲 Don't let your partner see your picture until they have finished. Were your coordinates accurate? How careful were they in following your instructions?

Points to remember

🔲 The design must be composed of straight lines.

🔲 The coordinates must be written in order, so that your partner can join them up.

🔲 You may have more than one set of coordinates, so that it is possible to have smaller shapes inside a larger one (for example, an eye).

Dear Helper
Discuss ideas for the coordinate picture. Direct your child towards designs that are suitable for constructing on a grid. Check that your child remembers that coordinates are worked out by reading the x axis first and then the y axis. As each coordinate is written down, ensure that your child writes it in the correct manner (for example, 3,2).

Name   Date

In a word

■ Find the correct operations to solve these word problems involving numbers and quantities. Remember to find an approximate answer first and check your solution at the end.

1. A train is scheduled to arrive at the station at 10.35am. It is delayed by one hour and forty-seven minutes. What time will it actually arrive?

2. There are 456 children in the school. 213 have a packed lunch, 54 go home and the rest have school dinners. How many children have school dinners?

3. Alan cycles 8.3km twice a day as he travels to and from school. How far does he travel in a fifteen-week school term?

4. A dog weighs 8.27kg. How many grams must it gain to weigh 14kg?

5. Sanjay and Nina grow 56 flowers. 15 die and 19 are damaged by the wind. How many flowers will they still have each if they share the rest out equally?

6. Carla wants to buy five CDs as presents. They cost £8.99 each. She has already saved £20.50. How much more money does she need?

7. It costs Sarah's mum £46 to fill her car tank with petrol. She travels an average of 250 miles on each tank. How many full tanks of petrol will she need to cover 2750 miles? How much will this cost her?

8. Sunil's train track measures 12.43m. Fiona's track measures 9.87m. Sunil's train goes six times around the track and Fiona's goes eight times. Whose train goes further and by how much?

BLOCK D

Dear Helper
Discussion will be a vital part of this activity. Talk through each of the problems with your child. Pay particular attention to picking out key words and numbers, working out approximate answers first, writing down calculations in the form of jottings and checking solutions at the end.

Name   Date

How big is the angle?

◀ Look carefully at each of these angles. Estimate the size of the angle, and then measure it carefully with a protractor. Remember that a right angle = 90°.

1.

Estimate _____

Measurement _____

2.

Estimate _____

Measurement _____

3.

Estimate _____

Measurement _____

4.

Estimate _____

Measurement _____

5.

Estimate _____

Measurement _____

6.

Estimate _____

Measurement _____

◀ Now draw these angles, using a protractor to measure accurately.

7. 69° angle   **8.** 101° angle   **9.** 88° angle

BLOCK D

Dear Helper
Encourage you child to look carefully at each angle and estimate the size. Remind them that a right angle is 90°, and that they should think about how much bigger or smaller it is than a right angle. When they have made and recorded the estimate, help them to carefully measure the angle, ensuring that the + on the protractor is positioned accurately. Talk to them about how good their estimate was, and remind them to refer to previous angles to help them improve their estimates.

Name	Date

Battleships

■ **Instructions – a game for two players**

- ☐ Cut the two grids from the bottom of this sheet and give one to each player.

- ☐ Without showing your partner, mark ten crosses in squares on your grid to represent battleships. Your partner does the same. Do not show each other your grids.

- ☐ Taking it in turns, try to shoot each other's battleships. Give a grid reference as a shot. If there is a battleship in an adjacent square to the grid reference, it is sunk. It is possible to sink more than one battleship with one shot.

- ☐ The winner is the first person to sink all the other player's battleships.

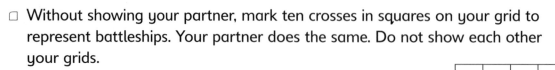

Shot – all these ships (x) would be sunk

Player 1

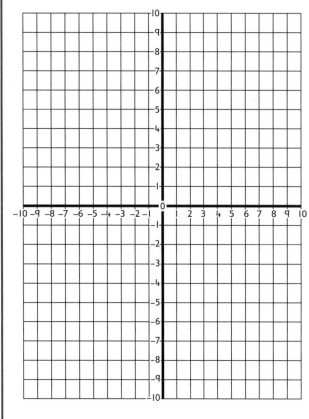

Player 2

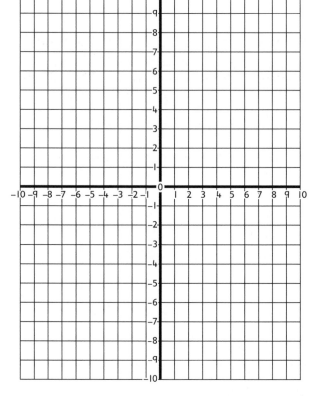

Dear Helper

This is a game for two players. Your child has learned about plotting coordinates. Remind them to remember where they have 'fired' and to think strategically. Encourage them to use all four quadrants.

Name   Date

Dream playground

■ You have the opportunity to design your own dream playground. You must include a hard play area and a grass area, but the rest is up to you. (For example, seating area, activity area with equipment.)

■ Draw a plan of your playground, showing measurements.

   ☐ Think about the scale for your plan.

   ☐ You may prefer to draw your plan on a larger piece of squared paper.

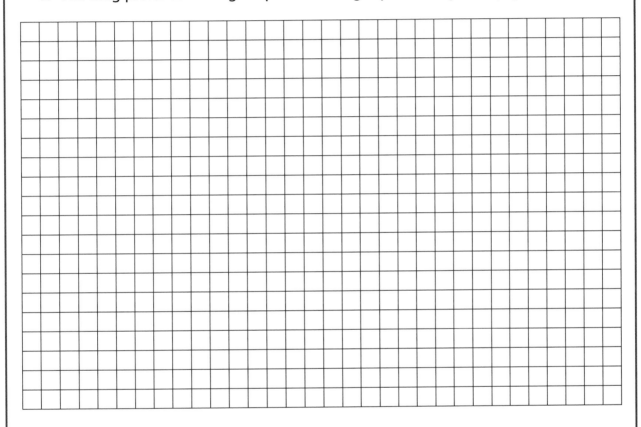

Scale: _____   Key: _____

■ When you have completed your design, calculate the area of grass and the area of hard play surface.

Area of grass: _____   Area of hard play surface: _____

Dear Helper
Your child has been learning about area and perimeter and how these fit into an overall design. This activity is designed to make your child think carefully about planning a playground area, taking into account measurements and the needs of the whole school community. Encourage them to think about where different areas should be sited. They can calculate the area of each irregular shape by counting the number of squares covered by the shape. Discuss the practicality of the design.

BLOCK D

Name

Date

Entertainment!

■ It is Mark's birthday and he is trying to decide how he would like to celebrate with his five best friends.

■ There are two options:

1. Bowling at TenPin Bowl with a take-away burger on the way home.

  ☐ Bowling costs £6.75 per person including shoe hire.

  ☐ Burgers cost £1.99 each.

2. A trip to the cinema followed by a pizza at the local Pizza Bar.

  ☐ Cinema tickets cost £4.25 each.

  ☐ There is a special deal at the Pizza Bar; a pizza of your choice and a soft drink for £4.50 each.

■ Work out the costs for each option and how much Mark will save if he chooses the cheaper option.

Remember to show your workings.

Dear Helper
This activity is designed to help your child apply the mathematics they have been learning to real events. Talk to them about the two different options, making sure that all the costs are included. Check the prices against local attractions and see if your child can suggest and cost other options.

BLOCK D

Name   Date

Bedroom furniture

◢ You will need some catalogues, newspapers or furniture brochures.

◢ Imagine you are furnishing your dream bedroom. Look in catalogues or advertisements to find the furniture you would like to buy.

◢ Draw a plan of your dream bedroom and show where you would place each item of furniture. Think about the size of your room and the scale you are using.

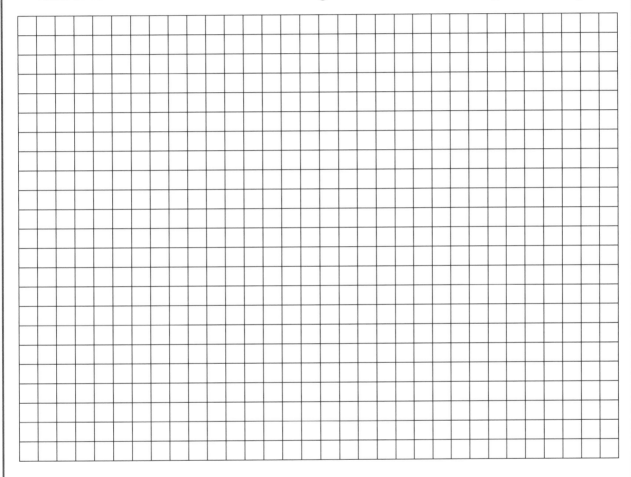

◢ Work out the costs for your furniture and make a shopping list.

_____

_____

_____

_____

Dear Helper
Talk to your child about what furniture and accessories may be needed in a dream bedroom. Help them to find items and the prices by looking in catalogues, newspapers, local shops or on the internet. Encourage them to think about what can be fitted into the room and to draw the plan to scale.

BLOCK D

Name   Date

Carpet fitter

◖ Mr and Mrs Prashad want to re-carpet their lounge. The measurements of the room are as follows:

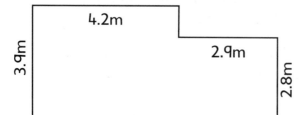

◖ The carpet they have chosen costs £16.95 per square metre, including free fitting.

   ☐ The carpet is plain and comes in 3m or 4m widths. Although it is better to have the carpet in one piece, it will join quite easily – but the carpet must be laid in the same direction.

   ☐ They also need underlay, which costs £1.99 per square metre. (Underlay can be joined in any direction.)

◖ Calculate how much carpet the Prashads will need to buy.
(Remember that they will have to pay for the 'wasted' carpet.)

◖ What is the cost of the 3m carpet? _____

◖ What is the cost of the 4m carpet? _____

◖ Which is more economical? _____

◖ What is the cost of the carpets and the underlay? _____

◖ Remember to show your workings. Show where the joins in the 3m carpet will be.

Dear Helper
Your child has been learning about the costs of redecorating and furnishing rooms and how to calculate costs. Encourage your child to work out the costs using both widths of carpet, discussing where there could be joins and the benefits of having no joins. Make sure that the costs for underlay are included.

Securing number facts, relationships and calculating

Activity name	Learning objectives	Managing the homework
E1		
How long? Complete a time log relating to journeys to school and use it to answer related questions.	Solve multi-step problems; choose and use appropriate calculation strategies at each stage, including calculator use	**Before:** Revise how to find an amount of time elapsed using the empty number line method. **After:** Compare the children's charts. Who has the longest/shortest travelling time?
Measure up Solve multi-step written problems.	Solve multi-step problems and problems involving fractions and decimals; choose and use appropriate calculation strategies at each stage, including calculator use	**Before:** Remind the children of the steps they need to go through when solving written problems. **After:** Choose one or two questions from the worksheet. Go through the strategies the children used to solve them.
Superleague Update a football league table using the match results.	Tabulate systematically the information in a problem or puzzle; identify and record the steps or calculations needed to solve it, using symbols where appropriate; interpret solutions in the original context and check their accuracy	**Before:** Remind the children that three points are awarded for a win and one for a draw. Explain that in football, goal difference can go into negative numbers, and that if two teams are level on points, goal difference is the deciding factor. **After:** Run through the team positions that the children have calculated. Ask: *Where have the greatest changes occurred? Which teams have changed places?*
Baking time Calculate the ingredients needed for making currant cakes for three and five people, based on a recipe for two people.	Solve simple problems involving direct proportion by scaling quantities up or down	**Before:** Work through several examples of similar problems involving ingredients. Stress the need to halve the amounts to find the ingredients needed for one person and then to multiply up. **After:** Go through the problem step by step and check that the correct solutions have been found. Discuss any alternative strategies the children might have used.
What do we need? Calculate costs for a barbecue, involving ratio and proportion.	• Solve multi-step problems and problems involving decimals; choose and use appropriate calculation strategies at each stage, including calculator use • Solve simple problems involving direct proportion by scaling quantities up or down	**Before:** Remind the children how to calculate costs for multiple quantities. Discuss what items might be needed for a barbecue. Explain to them what it means to 'break even'. **After:** Ask the children to explain how they calculated each cost. Ensure they have all understood that in some instances it is necessary to 'round up'.
Equal match Identify pairs of equivalent fractions or fraction and decimal equivalents.	Find equivalent decimals and fractions	**Before:** Remind the children how to identify equivalent fractions and how decimals can be converted to fractions. Make sure that they understand that 0.1 is $1/10$ and 0.01 is $1/100$. **After:** Discuss any difficulties that the children found. Ask them to tell you some pairs of equivalent fractions. Check that they can tell you fractions equivalent to 0.1 to 0.9.
E2		
Match it Match the improper fraction to corresponding mixed number.	Express a larger whole number as a fraction of a smaller one (for example, recognise that 8 slices of a 5-slice pizza represents $8/5$ or $1^3/5$ pizzas)	**Before:** Revise the terms 'mixed number' and 'improper fraction', and how to change between the two fraction forms. **After:** Go through the answers with the class. Ask: *Which two fractions do not match?*
Percentage maker 'Feed' numbers through a percentage function machine.	Find percentages of whole-number quantities (for example, 65% of £260)	**Before:** Remind the children how a function machine works. Revise fraction equivalents for simple percentages (for example, 25% = ¼). **After:** Check through the children's answers. Discuss how they calculated 15% of given numbers.
All in a day Work out what proportion of a day/week is spent engaged in various activities.	Solve simple problems involving direct proportion by scaling quantities up or down	**Before:** Show the children how you would work out the proportion of time spent on one activity during the day (for example, 2 hours watching TV would be $2/24$ or $1/12$). Explain that they will need to list each activity, work out the time spent and then round to the nearest hour, ensuring that the sum of all activities equals 24 hours. **After:** Ask the children to share their results. Was anyone surprised at how much time they spent during a week on any particular activity?

Securing number facts, relationships and calculating

Activity name	Learning objectives	Managing the homework
Family bingo Play fraction, decimal and percentage bingo.	Find equivalent percentages, decimals and fractions	**Before:** Make sure that the children have worked through examples of all the possible combinations (fraction to decimal, decimal to fraction, decimal to percentage, and so on). It may be necessary to demonstrate the game. **After:** Check through the questions to make sure the correct solutions were found. How long did it take to answer the questions mentally? Which questions were the easiest? Which proved to be the most difficult?
A good read Read several statements of information and deduce the answers to some questions.	Tabulate systematically the information in a problem or puzzle; identify and record the steps or calculations needed to solve it	**Before:** Ensure the children have some practice at interpreting information. Remind them that they must read through the information carefully and look for all the implications. **After:** Discuss any difficulties. If the children have drawn the wrong conclusions, encourage them to find where they went wrong.
Magic 4 × 4s Solve 4 × 4 magic squares.	Explain reasoning and conclusions, using words, symbols or diagrams as appropriate	**Before:** Recap the definition of a magic square. Show a simple example on the board. **After:** Go over the answers with the class. Discuss the approaches taken in order to arrive at a solution.
E3		
High Street Solve two problems involving percentages in a High Street scenario.	• Solve multi-step problems, and problems involving decimals and percentages; choose and use appropriate calculation strategies at each stage, including calculator use • Find percentages of whole-number quantities (for example, 65% of £260)	**Before:** Remind the children that at the shop percentage amounts should be calculated and then subtracted from the amount to find the sale price. At the building society percentage amounts should be added on to see how much the amounts have increased. Stress that calculators should be used when amounts become difficult. **After:** Ask: *Which of the two different tasks proved to be most difficult? Did the decimal point in the money amounts make calculating percentages easier or more difficult?* Ask the children to describe the strategy they used.
Fraction match Calculate fractions of different lengths and amounts of money, and match the question with its answer.	Find fractions of whole-number quantities (for example, $5/8$ of 96)	**Before:** Remind the children that when they multiply by a fraction the answer is smaller than the whole. Make sure that they understand how to use a calculator to check their answers when multiplying by a fraction. **After:** Discuss any difficulties, ensuring that the children used the correct calculation and included the correct units.
Four fractions in a row Complete a grid using fractions that total 2.	Tabulate systematically the information in a problem or puzzle; identify and record the steps or calculations needed to solve it; interpret solutions in the original context and check their accuracy	**Before:** Make sure that the children can add together simple fractions. Explain that this activity relies upon them thinking logically about how they can fit the four fractions into each row and column in the grid. **After:** Can the children design their own version of the grid, changing the fractions to make, for example, rows totalling 3?
Sale now on! Calculate the new cost of items after a percentage price reduction.	• Solve multi-step problems, and problems involving decimals and percentages; choose and use appropriate calculation strategies at each stage, including calculator use • Find percentages of whole-number quantities (for example, 65% of £260)	**Before:** Remind, or show, the children how to find 1, 5 and 10% of a figure. Give an example on the board. **After:** Suggest that the children could find examples of percentage reductions when next on a shopping trip. Check answers as a class.
Written methods Practise written methods of calculation for all four operations.	Use efficient written methods to add and subtract integers and decimals, to multiply and divide integers and decimals by a one-digit integer, and to multiply two-digit integers by a two-digit integer	**Before:** Go over the language used and ensure that the children are familiar with the term *product*. Are they familiar with the 'estimate, calculate then check' technique? **After:** Check answers and discuss the written methods used. Talk about the importance of setting out calculations neatly to reduce the risk of mistakes.
You're the teacher! Mark and correct answers to questions involving multiplication and division by 10/100/1000.	Use knowledge of place value and multiplication facts to derive related multiplication and division facts involving decimal numbers	**Before:** Ensure that the children are confident in their knowledge of multiplying and dividing by 10/100/1000. **After:** Check that the children have marked the answers correctly. Ask: *What mistakes did Dinesh make? What advice would you give him to improve his work?*

BLOCK E

■SCHOLASTIC

Name	Date

How long?

◼ Emma wants to find out how much walking she does each day. She keeps a time log to help her. Fill in the gaps.

Journey	Time started	Time finished	Time taken
Home to school	8.10am	8.35am	
School to home	3.15pm		25 minutes
To friend's house		4.18pm	23 minutes
To the swimming pool		6.40pm	35 minutes

◼ Pat the lorry driver has to complete a table of his journeys to give to his boss. How long did each journey take? Use the empty number lines to help you. The first line has some prompts to help you.

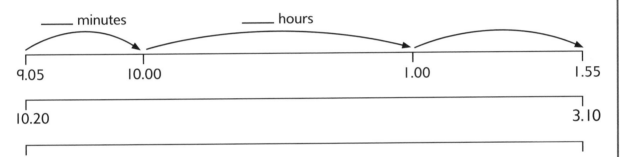

Journey	Time started	Time finished	Time taken
Day 1	9.05am	1.55pm	
Day 2	10.20am	3.10pm	
Day 3	4.45pm	11.20pm	
Day 4	8.25pm	2.05am	

☐ On Day 5, he leaves the depot at 11.35am. His journey takes 6 hours 15 minutes. What time does he arrive at his destination?

◼ Keep a time log of your journey to and from school each day for a week. Record the times in a log like Emma's. Add up the total time taken travelling in a week. Compare your times to other people in your class. Who has the longest/shortest journey? Did your journey take longer on some days than others? Why was this?

Dear Helper

Your child has been using empty number lines in class to help them find the amount of time elapsed. Ask them to show you how the method works. Check their understanding of the method before they attempt the homework.

BLOCK E

Name   Date

Measure up

■ Help the staff of Meadow Lane Primary School with their work. Show your workings on a separate sheet of paper and write your answers in the spaces provided.

1. Mrs Jones has to cover a large display board in the hall with frieze paper. The paper comes in rolls 50cm wide and 4 metres long. The display board is 10m long and 2m high. How many rolls of paper will she need?_____

2. Mr Price needs to paint the kick wall in the playground bright green. One litre of paint covers an area of 3 square metres. The kick wall measures 8m by $1\frac{1}{2}$m. How many litres of paint will he need? _____

3. The school day starts at 8.50am and ends at 3.15pm. There is a playtime break at 10.40am until 10.55am and a lunch break from 12 noon until 1.05pm.

    a) How long is the school day? _____

    b) How long do the children spend in lessons each day? _____

    c) How much playtime do the children have in a week? _____

4. The school has a Healthy Eating Tuck Shop.

    This is what they sell:

    | Fruit pot 20p   Wholemeal toast 15p |
    | Fruit juice 10p   Pot of raisins 15p |

    a) On the first day of school, 75 children buy a fruit pot and 59 children buy toast.

    How much money does Mrs Lemon the cook make? _____

    b) On the second day, £8.50 is spent on fruit juice and £9.30 on raisins.

    How many of each were sold? _____

5. The school playground measures 65m by 12m. What is its:

    a) perimeter? _____   b) area? _____

    c) It takes Mr Jones 40 seconds to sweep 20 square metres of the playground.

    How many minutes does it take to sweep the whole playground? _____

6. Mrs Lemon is baking a big cake for a school party. The ingredients here are for 20 people. What quantities of ingredients are needed to make a cake for 180 people?

    Ingredients   450g flour   225g butter
    220g caster sugar   3 eggs   75g jam
    175g icing sugar   2tbsp water

    _____

    _____

BLOCK E

Name	Date

Superleague

⬛ This is the top of the Superleague table. Teams are awarded three points for a win and one point for a draw.

TEAM	P	W	D	L	For	Against	Pts	GD
Rushall	8	6	1	1	37	12	19	25
Christchurch	7	5	2	0	29	16	17	13
Hamworthy	8	4	4	0	30	17	16	13
Burnham	8	4	4	0	25	19	16	6
Bloomfield	6	4	0	2	28	24	12	4
Cleeve	8	3	3	2	19	21	12	−2
Blanford	8	2	3	3	15	26	9	−11
Maldon	8	1	5	2	12	30	8	−18

⬛ Update the figures for the teams on the table above, to show the results given below. Re-order the teams to show their new positions in the league.

⬛ Now answer the following questions.

1. Who leads the league now?

2. Which team has scored the most goals?

3. Which team has let in the most goals?

4. Which team has the best goal difference?

5. Which team has the worst goal difference?

6. Which teams remain unbeaten?

RESULTS	
Christchurch 4	Selby 2
Cleeve 2	Bloomfield 2
Hamworthy 5	Boston 1
Burnham 0	Shildon 2
Hamble 3	Blanford 3
Rushall 1	Maldon 2

Dear Helper
Your child has been working on real-life problem solving, and football results and tables provide lots of maths to explore. Check that your child understands that three points are given for a win, one point for a draw and no points for a defeat. Ensure that they know that goal difference (GD) is calculated by finding the difference between the number of goals scored and the number of goals let in. Explain that seven goals scored and ten let in would produce a goal difference of −3. Also point out that, if teams are level on points, it is the goal difference that counts in calculating league positions.

Name _____ Date _____

Baking time

◼ These are the ingredients needed for making currant cakes for **two people.**

◼ How much of each ingredient would you need to make currant cakes for **three people?**

_____

_____

◼ How much of each ingredient would you need to make currant cakes for **five people?**

_____

_____

Currant cakes for two people
2 eggs
120g butter
220g flour
120g currants
60g sugar
60ml milk

◼ Answer the following questions for the cake recipe for **five people**.

1. I have only three eggs. How many more will I need? _____

2. I have 325g of butter. How much will I have left? _____

3. I have 300g of flour. How much more do I need? _____

4. I have 180g of currants. How much more do I need? _____

5. I have a quarter of a litre of milk. How much will I have left? _____

Dear Helper
This practical cooking problem is linked to activities your child has been doing at school on proportion and ratio. Proportion compares parts with the whole item, while ratio compares parts with parts. The easiest way of carrying out the calculations is to halve the ingredients to find out how much is needed for one person and then multiply up. As a further challenge, find ingredients in cookery books at home, round off the amounts and then carry out similar tasks.

Name	Date

What do we need?

◾ Park School PTA is having a barbecue.

    ☐ They are selling tickets at £2.50 each.

    ☐ Each ticket holder should have a chicken leg, a burger in a bap and a sausage, as well as a serving of salad.

◾ The cheapest prices the PTA could find are:

Bags of 20 chicken legs........................ £3.95

Pack of 12 burgers.............................. £1.40

Pack of 50 sausages........................... £2.50

Baps (pack of 24)............................... 75p

Salad bag (enough for ten helpings)... 99p

◾ In addition:

Tomato sauce (for 150 people).........£2.50

Brown sauce (for 150 people)...........£2.50

1. Work out the PTA's costs for catering for 150 people _____

2. How much profit will they make if they sell 150 tickets? _____

3. How many tickets will they need to sell to 'break even'? _____

Dear Helper

In class the children have been learning about costing events. Encourage your child to read the information carefully, and discuss the quantities that will be needed for each item. Make sure they realise that sometimes it will be necessary to buy more than is needed. Calculators may be used. Your child may like to cost prices for other items that could be sold at the barbecue.

BLOCK E

Name   Date

Equal match

◼ Match the equivalent values. One has already been done for you.

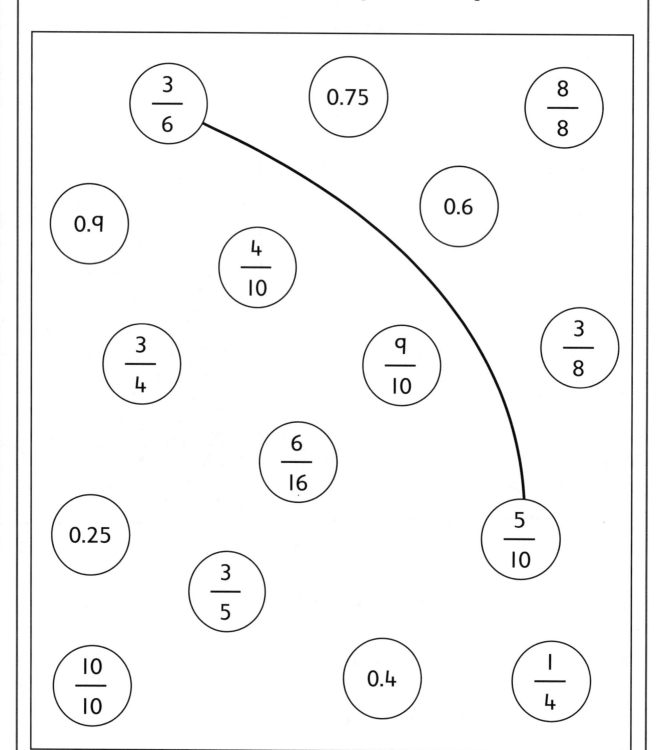

Dear Helper
This activity requires your child to think about equivalent fractions, and decimal equivalents. They need to work out the simplest form for each fraction and try to find a matching fraction or decimal. Ask your child to think of some other equivalent fractions for each value.

BLOCK E

Name	Date

Match it

📖 **Instructions – a game for two players**

- ☐ Cut out the fraction cards.

- ☐ Arrange them face down, keeping the improper fractions separate from the proper fractions.

- ☐ Each player takes it in turn to pick two cards, one from each group. If they match (for example, $\frac{32}{9} = 3\frac{5}{9}$) the player may keep the pair. If not, they should be put back, face down, in the same position.

- ☐ BEWARE! Two cards do not have a partner! When these two non-matching cards remain on the table, the game is over.

- ☐ The player with the most pairs wins.

- ☐ Repeat the game until you feel confident changing improper fractions to mixed numbers.

📖 Can you explain why the two remaining cards do not match? Use two blank playing cards to write a partner for each one.

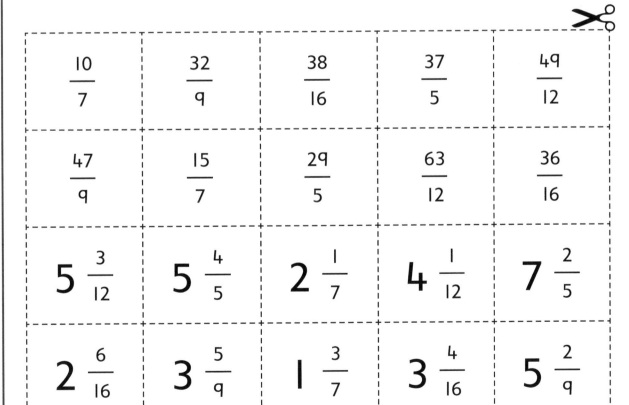

$\frac{10}{7}$	$\frac{32}{9}$	$\frac{38}{16}$	$\frac{37}{5}$	$\frac{49}{12}$
$\frac{47}{9}$	$\frac{15}{7}$	$\frac{29}{5}$	$\frac{63}{12}$	$\frac{36}{16}$
$5\frac{3}{12}$	$5\frac{4}{5}$	$2\frac{1}{7}$	$4\frac{1}{12}$	$7\frac{2}{5}$
$2\frac{6}{16}$	$3\frac{5}{9}$	$1\frac{3}{7}$	$3\frac{4}{16}$	$5\frac{2}{9}$

Dear Helper
This homework will help your child to reinforce work they have been doing in class. Allow your child to work through this activity without support so that the game can come to a winning conclusion. Ask them to explain the process they have used and how they found the correct pair.

Name   Date

Percentage maker

■ Feed the numbers through the percentage machines to complete each chart. The first one has been partly filled in.

1. 60   80   120   68   200

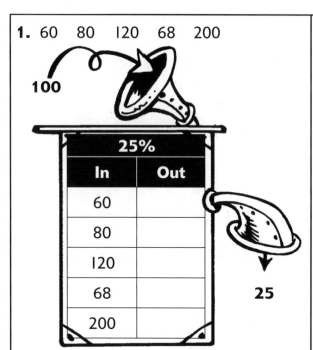

100

25%	
In	Out
60	
80	
120	
68	
200	

25

2. £500   180   320cm   96   £1.60

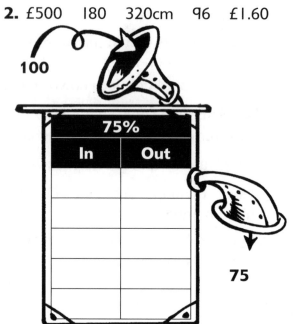

100

75%	
In	Out

75

3. 100   600   £4·60   £75   1600

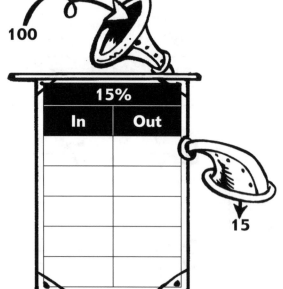

100

15%	
In	Out

15

4. £1760   £1·50   320   15 metres   25

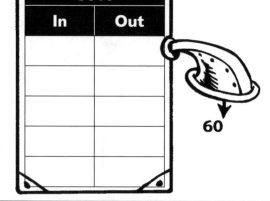

100

60%	
In	Out

60

Dear Helper
Reinforce the link between fractions and percentages to help your child work out the answers. Discuss that 25% is ¼, 75% is ¾ and 60% is ⁶/₁₀. Discuss how 15% could be found. Your child should suggest find 10% first, then halve to give 5% then add together.

BLOCK E

Name	Date

All in a day

🔳 Have you ever wondered how you spend your time each day? Let's find out!

🔳 First of all, on a separate sheet of paper, list all of the activities you do during a school day – for example, eating, travelling, sleeping and so on. Estimate how long you spend on each one.

🔳 Keep a log of everything you actually do during a day. For example, 15 minutes eating, 30 minutes playing football, 1 hour watching television, 20 minutes eating, and so on. The next morning, write down how long you were asleep.

🔳 Add up all the time you spent on each activity and round the result up or down to the nearest hour. For example, 10 minutes for breakfast + 20 minutes for lunch + 20 minutes for tea = 50 minutes, rounded to the nearest hour = 1 hour eating. Make sure all of your activities add up to 24 hours.

🔳 Now fill in the chart below, writing each activity as a proportion of the day. For example, 2 hours spent playing would be a proportion of $\frac{2}{24}$ or $\frac{1}{12}$.

Activity	Number of hours	Proportion

🔳 Compare these results to your estimates. Were there any surprises? Did you spend longer on something than you thought?

🔳 Challenge yourself to work out how long you spend on each activity in a week, a month or even a year!

Dear Helper
Support your child in calculating how they spend their day. Ensure that the rounding up or down of the hours equates to 24 hours. Discuss ways in which your child could work out how long they spend on each activity in a week, month or year.

BLOCK E

Name	Date

Family bingo

■ Four people are playing a game of family bingo; Mr Lucky, Miss Chance, Ms Gamble and Mrs Bonus. Below are the set of clues that are going to be called out.

■ Work through the clues in the correct order, crossing off the answers on each of the cards to find out who is the winner of the game (that is, the player with all the numbers crossed off first).

Clues

1. $\frac{1}{2}$ as a decimal

2. $\frac{1}{4}$ as a percentage

3. 10% as a fraction

4. 75% as a fraction

5. $\frac{8}{10}$ as a decimal

6. $\frac{6}{10}$ as a percentage

7. $\frac{3}{10}$ as a percentage

8. 0.5 as a fraction

9. 20% as a decimal

10. $\frac{1}{10}$ as a percentage

11. $\frac{3}{4}$ as a percentage

12. $\frac{7}{10}$ as a percentage

Mr Lucky

90%	$\frac{3}{4}$	$\frac{1}{4}$	
		20%	$\frac{1}{10}$
75%	0.5		
			$\frac{1}{2}$

Miss Chance

0.2		40%	
	$\frac{1}{8}$		60%
		$\frac{1}{10}$	
0.5		0.7	$\frac{3}{4}$

Ms Gamble

25%			$\frac{3}{4}$
40%		10%	
	0.8		$\frac{1}{2}$
$\frac{1}{10}$			30%

Mrs Bonus

	0.5		$\frac{1}{10}$
$\frac{1}{2}$			0.8
	$\frac{3}{4}$	25%	
70%			30%

■ Who was the winner of the game? _____

Dear Helper
Let your child do the marking on all four cards while you act as the caller. Talk to your child first about the fact that exactly the same amounts can be given as a fraction, a decimal and a percentage – for example, ½, 0.5 and 50%. Give your child plenty of time to mark the four cards and provide help with some of the more difficult calculations.

BLOCK E

Name	Date

A good read

◼ Three bookshops have been chosen to launch the latest books by three authors – James Eagle, Sheila Sparrow and George Gull. Each bookshop will only feature one book.

◼ From the four pieces of information supplied, work out:

☐ Which author is being promoted by which shop?

☐ In what month will the launch of each book take place?

☐ What type of book has each author written?

1. The author of the adventure story will not be at the January launch of her book.

2. Super Bookstore is the only bookshop that stocks biographies.

3. James Eagle's book will not be launched in the shortest month, nor will it be on sale in Choice Books.

4. The book launched in April was the first biography that the author has written.

◼ Use this table to help you sort out the information. Remember to complete as many boxes as you can.

	James Eagle	Sheila Sparrow	George Gull	January	March	April	Adventure	Biography	Science fiction
Bargain Read									
Choice Books									
Super Bookstore									
Adventure									
Biography									
Science fiction									
January									
March									
April									

◼ Write your solution in the grid below.

Bookshop	Author	Launch month	Book type

Dear Helper
Encourage your child to read through the information carefully and mark a tick or a cross on the chart as they establish facts. Make sure they think about all aspects of the information. Talk to them about how information may be worded and encourage them to look for 'hidden' information.

BLOCK E

Name   Date

Magic 4 × 4s

- This is a 4 × 4 magic square. The totals of each row and column add up to 40.

10	7	4	19	**40**
5	18	11	6	**40**
17	2	9	12	**40**
8	13	16	3	**40**
40	**40**	**40**	**40**	

- There are 74 combinations for 4 × 4 magic squares that add up to 40!

- Using the information you have on this sheet, complete this 4 × 4 magic square so that each row and column adds up to 40.

				40
				40
				40
				40
40	**40**	**40**	**40**	

- Now complete this 4 × 4 magic square so that the rows and columns add up to 50.

				50
				50
				50
				50
50	**50**	**50**	**50**	

Dear Helper

This activity will help your child to understand the need to work logically to solve some problems. Encourage your child to explain their reasoning. They should be able to complete the first part of this task by adding and subtracting from the numbers given in the example. They can then use the same technique to solve the second grid so that each row and column totals 50.

Name	Date

High Street

◼ Find out how much the items in this shop window have been reduced by and calculate the new sale price for each. You may need to round up the answer.

SALE BARGAINS	**Camera £40** **10% OFF**	**Watch £25** **20% OFF**	**TV £150** **5% OFF**
BIKE £95 15% OFF	**Trainers** **£24.99** **20% OFF**	**Radio** **£45.98** **25% OFF**	**Computer** **Monitor £99** **5% OFF**
Jeans £10.50 10% OFF			

☐ Copy and complete this table to record your answers for the items listed above.

Item	Cost	Reduction	Sale price
camera	£40	£4	£36

◼ Find out how much interest each child earns on their account in the Building Society and calculate the amount of savings they will have at the end of the year.

MOORCROFT BUILDING SOCIETY	**15% interest for new savers**	David £10 Jamil £24 Sunita £18	Sarah £56 Emma £37 Sanjay £105

☐ Copy and complete this table to record your answers for all the children listed.

Name	Amount	Interest	Total
David	£10	£1.50	£11.50

BLOCK E

Dear Helper
Encourage your child to work out solutions mentally or by using pencil-and-paper methods wherever possible, but calculators may be needed in some cases. Ask your child to explain to you the method they are going to use for finding percentages before they start. Stress the importance of the decimal point in money amounts. Point out that percentage amounts must be subtracted in the case of sale items but added on in the case of Building Society interest.

Name | Date

Fraction match

◼ Look carefully at the fraction calculation in the first column and match it with its answer in the second column. Use a watch to time how long it takes you to complete the activity.

A	$\frac{3}{4}$ of 2m 60cm
B	$\frac{2}{5}$ of 4m 90cm
C	$3\frac{1}{3} \times £3.00$
D	$\frac{1}{5}$ of £51
E	$2\frac{3}{4} \times £3.60$
F	$1\frac{1}{4} \times 1\frac{1}{2}$ m
G	$\frac{1}{3}$ of £30.90
H	$\frac{3}{8}$ of 5.1m
I	$\frac{2}{5} \times £24$
J	$2\frac{1}{2} \times 77$cm

1	192.5cm
2	191.25cm
3	£9.90
4	196cm
5	£9.60
6	£10.20
7	195cm
8	£10.30
9	£10
10	187.5cm

◼ Time taken: _____ minutes _____ seconds.

◼ Use a calculator to check your answers.

Dear Helper

This is a timed activity in which your child needs to find fractions of amounts. There are a number of answers that are similar so it is important to make sure your child works out each calculation carefully. Encourage him/her to work quickly but accurately and record the time taken. Afterwards your child may check answers using a calculator.

BLOCK E

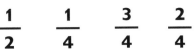

Name	Date

Four fractions in a row

◀ Complete the grid so that these four fractions appear only once in each row and each column:

$\dfrac{1}{2}$ $\dfrac{1}{4}$ $\dfrac{3}{4}$ $\dfrac{2}{4}$

◀ The sum of each row and each column should be 2.

◀ The sum of the diagonals must be 2 and the sum of the four fractions in any of the four blocks of four squares must be 2.

$\dfrac{1}{4}$			
			$\dfrac{2}{4}$
	$\dfrac{1}{2}$		

◀ List some other sets of four fractions that total 2.

_____

_____

_____

_____

Dear Helper
Your child has been learning about equivalent fractions and simple addition of fractions. This activity encourages them to think logically while developing confidence with simple addition of fractions.

BLOCK E

Name   Date

Sale now on!

◼ Look at these items on display in the winter sale of the Smith and Jones department store. Write the new prices on the price tags.

◼ Daniel works at Smith and Jones and gets a staff discount of 12%. He buys a sofa and a dining table in the sale.

◼ How much does Daniel pay for them both after his staff discount has been taken off the sale price?

Dear Helper

This activity will help your child to understand the use of percentages in a real-life context. Your child could use a calculator for this activity but may wish to try without first. You can remind them that in order to find 1% of something, you can start by finding 10% and then 10% again. You can work out any percentage by adding the 10%, 5% and 1% answers together!

Name	Date

Written methods

◼ Try these calculations involving all four operations. Use a written method you have been taught at school.

Addition

1. What is the total of 783 and 468? _____

2. Increase 529 by 825. _____

3. Add 73, 48 and 97. _____

Subtraction

4. 5839 subtract 3167. _____

5. How much less is 426 than 895? _____

6. What is the difference between 591 and 837? _____

Multiplication

7. What is 72 multiplied by 53? _____

8. What is the product of 87 and 78? _____

9. What is 46 times 44? _____

Division

10. How many times does 4 fit into 852? _____

11. What is 773 divided by 6? _____

12. What is the remainder when 84 is shared by 7? _____

Dear Helper
This activity will provide your child with practice of choosing the most appropriate method to calculate an answer. By Year 6, your child should be familiar with a variety of written methods. Long multiplication and long division will have been taught in class. It really helps if they set their work out clearly and neatly. This will help prevent errors when calculating in columns.

Name	Date

You're the teacher!

- ◼ It's your turn to mark some work!
- ◼ For his homework, Dinesh had to multiply and divide by 10, 100 and 1000.
- ◼ He has finished his homework but didn't check his answers!
- ◼ Check his work carefully and mark his answers.
- ◼ Write the correct answer next to any of his answers that are incorrect.

1. $5.21 \times 100 = 52.1$

2. $725 \div 10 = 72.5$

3. $397 \times 10 = 3970$

4. $42.8 \div 100 = 4280$

5. $0.213 \times 1000 = 21.3$

6. $1.23 \div 10 = 0.123$

7. $54.9 \times 100 = 549$

8. $676 \div 1000 = 0.676$

9. $1.45 \times 1000 = 1450$

10. $993 \div 100 = 0.993$

11. $4.56 \times 10 = 0.456$

12. $782 \div 1000 = 0.782$

13. $4.66 \times 100 = 466$

14. $29.1 \div 10 = 291$

15. $2.03 \times 1000 = 2300$

Dear Helper

This activity will help your child to multiply and divide decimals by 10, 100 and 1000. It should also emphasise the need for them to check their own answers! Ask your child to explain how to multiply and divide by 10, 100 and 1000. They should know that the digits move to the left when they multiply by one of these numbers and the digits move to the right when they divide by one of these numbers.

BLOCK E

Puzzles and problems: Objectives grid

The puzzles and problems activities can be used very flexibly to provide children with fun maths tasks to take home. The puzzles and problems are based on work that children will be covering during the year and should test their use and application of mathematics at an appropriate level. Where possible, children should be encouraged to try different approaches to solving these problems and to look for clues and patterns in mathematics.

The grid below lists each activity and identifies links to the different objectives within the Using and applying mathematics strand of the Renewed Framework.

	Solve multi-step problems, and problems involving fractions, decimals and percentages; choose and use appropriate calculation strategies at each stage	Identify and record the calculations needed to solve a problem or puzzle, using symbols where appropriate; interpret solutions in the original context and check their accuracy	Collect, organise and represent information, interpret results and review methods; identify and answer related questions	Represent and interpret sequences, patterns and relationships involving numbers and shapes; construct and use simple expressions and formulae in words then symbols	Explain reasoning and conclusions, using words, symbols or diagrams as appropriate
1 Chilly Billy				✔	
2 What's the question?					✔
3 What's my number?	✔				
4 School long jump	✔				
5 Texting totals	✔				
6 On the river	✔				
7 That's square, man!	✔				
8 Prime time		✔			
9 Parallel lines				✔	
10 Kite design				✔	
11 Algy and Brian	✔				
12 Prove Penny wrong				✔	
13 Guilders for Gail	✔				
14 Seven-loving Sven			✔		
15 Happy hundred!			✔		
16 Car colours survey			✔		
17 Tea breaks	✔				
18 Christmas turkey	✔				
19 How likely?					✔
20 Invisible ink	✔				
21 Goal!	✔				
22 Pick 'n' mix	✔				
23 Swimming pool				✔	
24 Fish 'n' chips	✔				
25 Model plane	✔				
26 In the middle	✔				
27 Moon traveller	✔				
28 Pizza delivery	✔				
29 Battle of the bands	✔				
30 Fruit punch			✔		
31 Blewett Hall	✔				
32 Haunted cellar	✔				
33 Peckish peacocks	✔				
34 Jumping Jacks	✔				
35 Sponsored silence	✔				
36 Cut-price car	✔				

1 Chilly Billy

Chilly Billy is in Iceland where the temperature is −14 degrees.

Sunshine Sue is in Florida where the temperature is 33 degrees.

What is the difference between the two temperatures?

2 What's the question?

Professor M. T. Thorts says the answer to his question is 14.8.

Write three possible questions he might have asked.

Puzzles and problems

3 What's my number?

Professor M. T. Thorts is thinking of a number.

He adds 6 and multiplies the answer by 6.

He says the answer is 108.

What number was the Professor thinking of?

4 School long jump

Jesse jumps 3.12m in the long jump and wins the bronze medal.

Carl jumps 3.17m to win the gold.

Bob wins silver by jumping the distance exactly halfway between Jesse and Carl's jumps.

How far did Bob jump?

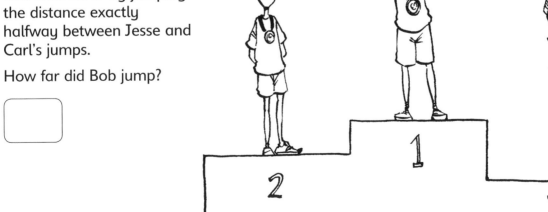

5 Texting totals

The first 500 texts sent from Moby's mobile cost 3p each.

Messages after this cost Moby 2.5p each.

Moby sends 1028 messages in six months.

How much does this cost him in total?

6 On the river

It costs £9.50 to hire a boat for a day on the river.

The five-piece boy band Tone Def decide to hire one.

They share the cost equally.

How much do they pay each?

Puzzles and problems

7 That's square, man!

Willow the hippy is thinking about square numbers. How square!

She has found two that total 100.

Which two square numbers is Willow thinking of?

8 Prime time

Willow loves prime numbers.

She has thought of a prime number under 100.

Its digits total 17, which is also a prime number.

Which prime number was Willow thinking of?

9 Parallel lines

Look at this cuboid.

How many lines are parallel to the one that is highlighted?

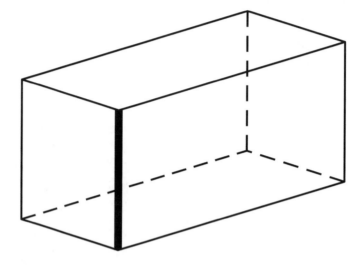

10 Kite design

Kevin drew a design for a kite.

He started to count the number of triangles which he saw in the shape.

Kevin found five but he was wrong.

How many triangles are there in Kevin's design?

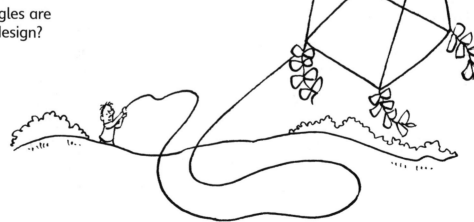

PHOTOCOPIABLE ■SCHOLASTIC

Puzzles and problems

11 Algy and Brian

Algy and Brian each represent a different number.

Algy is the number 26.

Algy + Algy = Brian + Brian + Algy

How much is Brian worth?

12 Prove Penny wrong

Penny says that pentagons don't contain any right angles.

Draw a pentagon that contains three right angles to prove her wrong!

Prove me wrong.

13 Guilders for Gail?

In Aruba the currency used is the guilder.

The exchange rate is 2.4 guilder to £1.

Gail travels to Aruba and changes £500 into guilders.

How many guilders does Gail get for her £500?

14 Seven-loving Sven

Sven's lucky number is 7.

He loves the number so much he pinches them whenever he can!

In a street with house numbers from 1 to 100 Sven pinched all the 7 digits from the front doors.

How many 7s did Sven pinch?

15 Happy hundred!

Jeanne Calment from France is thought to have been the world's oldest living person.

She lived until she was 122 years old!

How many days is it until your 100th birthday?

Hint

Don't forget leap years! (2008 was a leap year)

16 Car colours survey

Lewis carried out a survey to find out which was the most popular car colour.

He watched from his window for one hour and found that red cars went past the most often.

Conduct your own survey on car colour.

You can do this from home or when you are next on a car journey.

Do your results show the same conclusion as Lewis?

17 Tea breaks

Builder Justin drinks six cups of tea a day.

Each cup holds 275ml of tea.

How many litres of tea does Justin drink each day?

18 Christmas turkey

Aunt Ethel has bought a turkey from the butcher.

It weighs 7 kilograms.

However, Aunt Ethel only understands imperial measurements so she weighs things in pounds and ounces.

How heavy is the turkey in pounds and ounces?

Hint 1kg = 2.2lb

The turkey needs to be cooked for 20 minutes per pound plus 20 minutes.

How long will Aunt Ethel's turkey take to cook?

19 How likely?

Tick the correct box for each of these statements.	certain	likely	unlikely	impossible
Mr Spaceman is living in a retirement flat on Jupiter				
The next Prime Minister of the United Kingdom will be called Daisy the cow				
There will be rain in London next April				
My pet hamster will learn how to fly a jumbo jet				
If I jump in the sea, I will get wet				

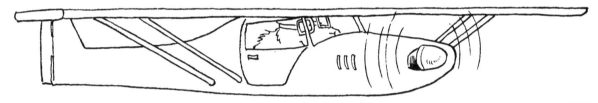

20 Invisible ink

A bottle contains one litre of invisible ink.

Barry pours out five measures of 125ml to his friends.

How much invisible ink does he have left? (Don't say you don't know because it's invisible!)

Puzzles and problems

21 Goal!

Mudworth United scored 65, 44, 53 and 58 goals in four seasons.

What was the mean number of goals they scored each season?

Hint

The mean is the average number.

22 Pick 'n' mix

Pick 'n' mix sweets cost 80p for 100g.

Josh spends his £2 coin on a bagful.

How many grams of sweets does Josh get?

Puzzles and problems

23 Swimming pool

The area of a swimming pool is 160m^2.

One of the sides is 20m.

What is the perimeter of the swimming pool?

24 Fish 'n' chips

Shane goes to the chip shop with his friend Wayne.

Shane spends £3.

He buys a jumbo piece of cod for £1.80 and two portions of chips.

How much does one portion of chips cost?

25 **Model plane**

Doug has built a 12cm long model World War II Spitfire fighter plane.

It is 72 times smaller than a real Spitfire.

How long was a real Spitfire?

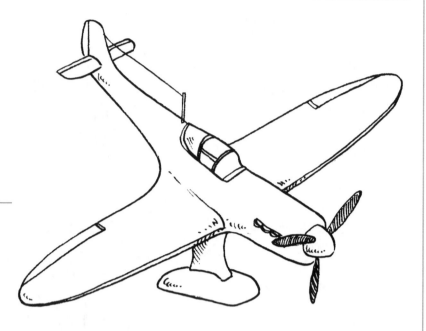

26 **In the middle**

Jenny is 94cm tall.

Benny is 1.36m tall.

Penny's height is exactly halfway between Jenny's and Benny's.

How tall is Penny?

Puzzles and problems

27 Moon traveller

The moon is approximately 384,000km from Earth.

Five miles is approximately eight kilometres.

Approximately how many miles are there between the moon and Earth?

28 Pizza delivery

Paulo and his three friends order nine mini pizzas.

They divide the pizzas equally between them.

How much pizza do they get each?

29 Battle of the bands

The new bands Kneecap and Ankle are performing concerts.

Kneecap charge £1.25 a ticket and 175 people come to their concert.

Ankle charge £1.35 a ticket and 160 people come to their concert.

Which band takes the most money and by how much?

_____

_____

30 Fruit punch

Freya makes a fruit punch for three people. She uses:

1 ½ litres lemonade

4 oranges

3 limes

200g sugar

300g strawberries

Rewrite the recipe so there is enough fruit punch for nine people.

_____

_____

_____

Puzzles and problems

31 Blewett Hall

Lord Blewett was broke so he opened up his home to the public.

50,000 visitors came in one year!

15% visited in May and 45% visited in August.

How many visitors came in the rest of the year?

32 Haunted cellar

Five hundred visitors to Blewett Hall went on a tour of the haunted cellar.

Three quarters of them said they saw a ghost!

How many visitors didn't see a ghost?

33 Peckish peacocks

Lord Blewett charges visitors 40p for 100g of bird seed to feed his peacocks.

Sasha pays £2 for a bag of birdseed.

How many grams does she get?

34 Jumping Jacks

Jack jumped 5.3m off a ramp on his motorbike.

Jackie jumped half this distance on her bicycle.

How many centimetres did Jackie jump?

Puzzles and problems

35 Sponsored silence

Loudmouth Larry is sponsored £1.25 for every hour he keeps his big mouth shut!

Larry manages to keep quiet for 112 hours.

How much money does he raise for charity?

36 Cut-price car

Grant wants to sell his car for £600 but the best price he is offered is 20% less.

What was the best price Grant was offered?

Block A

P9   **Divide me** 981 ÷ 9 = 109; 264 ÷ 12 = 22; 966 ÷ 7 = 138; 1232 ÷ 11 = 112; 704 ÷ 4 = 176; 1530 ÷ 15 = 102; 4976 ÷ 8 = 622; 2050 ÷ 10 = 205; 894 ÷ 6 = 149; 576 ÷ 18 = 32

P10 **Positive and negative** **1** −2; **2** −4; **3** −6; **4** 0, 3, 6; **5** −2, −6, −10; **6** 6, 4, 2, 0, −1, −3; **7** −8, −4, −2, 0, 5, 7

P11 **Guitar Genius** Eric: 2.225, 2.553, 5.225, 5.552
Josh: 0.202, 1.002, 1.221, 2.101
Ganesh: 4.504, 4.554, 5.445, 5.545
Katy: 13.367, 13.673, 13.763, 31.352
Alesha: 23.223, 23.322, 32.332, 33.323

P12 **Decimal dash!** **1** 1.5; **2** 2.4; **3** 5.6; **4** 2.7; **5** 2; **6** 5.6; **7** 0.9; **8** 2.4; **9** 1; **10** 0.4; **11** 0.9; **12** 0.3; **13** 0.8; **14** 0.7; **15** 0.7; **16** 0.6; **17** 0.9; **18** 0.8

P13 **One of each** **1** 8 × 2.5 = 20; **2** 12 × 4.25 = 51; **3** 4 × 9.75 = 39; **4** 5 × 5.6 = 28; **5** 6 × 12.5 = 75; **6** 6 × 2.5 = 15; **7** 8 × 12.5 = 100; **8** 12 × 9.75 = 117

P14 **On the grid** **1** 245 × 47 = 11,515; **2** 592 × 27 = 15,984; **3** 765 × 58 = 44,370

P15 **What's missing?** **1** How many children attend Gym Club? **2** How many cards does Emma have? **3** How long does each lesson last? **4** How many pens are there? **5** How far does Stacey swim at weekends? **6** What is the length of one side of the garden?

P16 **Missing digits** **1** 273.5 × 8 = 2188; **2** 78.36 ÷ 3 = 26.12; **3** 3.25 + 170.02 + 103.5 + 5.87 = 282.64; **4** 17.28 × 7 = 120.96; **5** 7.124 × 3 = 21.372; **6** 6.91 × 35 = 241.85

P17 **Nearest wins** No answers

P18 **Swamp fever** **1** 265, 312, 75, 98, 250 or 265, 123, 75, 189, 98, 250; **2** 5111, 4661, 2080, 1816

P19 **Shop 'til you drop** No answers

Block B

P23 **Multiplying and dividing** No answers

P24 **Name that shape** **1** Regular trapezium; **2** Kite; **3** Square or rhombus; **4** Parallelogram or rhombus; **5** Rhombus; **6** Trapezium

P25 **What's next?** **1** 43, 52, 62; Rule: increase number added by 1
2 14, 8, 5; Rule: halve amount subtracted
3 64, 81, 100; Rule: increase number added by 2 (also, they are all square numbers in ascending order)

4 $^8/_{32}$, $^{16}/_{64}$, $^{32}/_{128}$; Rule: double numerator and denominator
5 M, S, Z; Rule: increase interval between letters by 1
6 202, 607, 1822; Rule: increase interval between numbers by ×3

P26 **What's it worth?** $a^2 = 16$; 2b = 6; 7c + 3b = 58; ed = 45; $(ba)^2 = 144$; eb = 27; 2d + 6b = 28; 2d × 6 = 60; 4e ÷ 2b = 6; e ÷ b = 3; bc = 21

P27 **Fancy boxes** There are 11 different nets for a cube

P28 **Floor shapes** Answers will vary

P29 **Boxed in** **1** 10, 35, 30; 45, 25, 5; 20, 15, 40; **2** $^1/_4$, $1^1/_8$, $^1/_2$; $^7/_8$, $^5/_8$, $^3/_8$; $^3/_4$ (or $^6/_8$) $^1/_8$, 1; **3** 0.6, 0.7, 0.2; 0.1, 0.5, 0.9; 0.8, 0.3, 0.4; **4** −2, 3, 2; 5, 1, −3; 0, −1, 4; **5** 2, 5, 7, 12, 19; **6** 3, 6, 9, 15, 24; **7** 1, 3½, 4½, 8, 12½

P30 **Euler's rule** No answers

P31 **Letter time** **1** 19; **2** 40; **3** 48; **4** 2; **5** 35; **6** 3; **7** 12; **8** 10; **9** 21; **10** 26; **11** 3; 5; 7; 9; 11; **12** 2; 3; 4; 5; 6; **13** 2; 5; 8; 11; 14 **14** 0; 1; 2; 3

P32 **Jumping frogs** **1** Rule +2, +3; continues 15, 17, 20, 22
2(a) Rule +4, +3; continues 18, 21, 25, 28
(b) Rule +6, +3; continues 24, 27, 33, 36
(c) Rule +7, +5; continues 31, 36, 43, 48
3 Rule −3, −2; continues 38, 36, 33, 31

P33 **How old are they?** **1** 6; **2** 39; **3** 30; **4** 27; **5** 8; **6** 57; **7** 4; **8** 48

P34 **Build it** No answers

P35 **Day out** **1** $2^8/_{14}$ or 2.57 or 2 r8, round up to 3; **2** $20^4/_{10}$ or 20.4 or 20 r4, round up to 21; **3** $3^4/_{32}$ or 3.125 or 3 r4, round down to 3; **4** $3^6/_{10}$ or 3.6 or 3 r6, round up to 4; **5** $4^4/_5$ or 4.8 or 4 r4, round up to 5; **6** $5^{25}/_{35}$ or 5.71 or 5 r25, round down to 5

P36 **Best buy** Per 100ml:
Orange 500ml = 14p, 1 litre = 12p, 2 litres = 6p;
Lemonade 500ml = 6p, 1 litre = 4p, 2 litres = 3p;
Water 500ml = 8p, 1 litre = 6p, 2 litres = 4p

P37 **Squares of multiples of 10** *Between 2000 and 5000:* 50 × 50 = 2500, 60 × 60 = 3600, 70 × 70 = 4900; *Between 1000 and 10,000:* 40 × 40 = 1600, 50 × 50 = 2500, 60 × 60 = 3600, 70 × 70 = 4900, 80 × 80 = 6400, 90 × 90 = 8100

P38 **Prime numbers up to 100** Prime numbers: 2, 3, 5, 7, 11, 13, 17, 19, 23, 29, 31, 37, 41, 43, 47, 53, 59, 61, 67, 71, 73, 79, 83, 89, 97

P39 **Properties of numbers** **1** 16, 32, 40; **2** 48;
3 64, 88; **4** 18, 30; **5** 12, 24, 36; **6** 42, 54, 72
7 12, 21, 33; **8** 21, 36, 48; **9** 75, 84, 87, 93;
10 45, 54, 72; **11** 108, 144; **12** 702, 9783

P40 **Wedding madness!** Meal £25,116; Champagne
£39,600; Band £11,375; Flowers £3,492.50;
Goody bags £84,525; Taxis £3,604; Total cost
£167,712.50; 839 weeks (over 16 years!)

Block C

P43 **What's on?** Answers will vary

P44 **A good guess** Answers will vary

P45 **My day** Answers will vary

P46 **Dicey Dave** 10 and 11 are the most likely
totals; 3 and 18 are the least likely totals

P47 **What's the chance?** Answers will vary

P48 **Make a guess** Answers will vary

P49 **How many koruna?** **1** £32.74; **2** 610 koruna

P50 **Island Paradisio temperatures** **1** 26°C; **2** 7°C;
3 26°C; **4** 26°C; **5** mode: 28°C, range: 9°C,
median: 28°C, mean: 30°C; **6** mode: 28°C, range:
12°C, median: 28°C, mean: 28°C

P51 **In a spin** Chance of landing on a 5 = $^3/_8$;
Landing on an even number = $^3/_8$; Landing on an
odd number = $^5/_8$

P52 **Book your own break** Answers will vary

P53 **Ferry crossing** **1** £280; **2** £280 − 40% =
£168; **3** £200 − 20% = £160; **4** (£50 +£45) × 2
= £190

P54 **Island Paradisio rainfall** **1** Justine is incorrect
because the mean is lower than the amount of
rain every month; **2** 13mm; **3** Answers will
vary; **4** 6mm; **5** Answers will vary

Block D

P57 **Use your loaf** Answers will vary

P58 **Mr Fixit**

Length	Width	Perimeter
60m	1m	122m
30m	2m	64m
20m	3m	46m
15m	4m	38m
12m	5m	34m
10m	6m	32m

P59 **Give me room** *Areas:* **1** 36m²; **2** 42m²;
3 52m²; **4** 52m²; **5** 39m²; **6** 57m²; room 6 has
the largest area. *Perimeters:* **1** 26m; **2** 31m;
3 30m; **4** 34m; **5** 30m; **6** 36m

P60 **Supermarket shopping** **1** £4.58; **2** 22p;
3 £1.80; **4** 70p; **5** 22p; **6** 24p; **7** £3.25;
8 £22.02

P61 **Picture this** Answers will vary

P62 **In a word** **1** 12.22pm; **2** 189; **3** 1245km;
4 5730g; **5** 11 each; **6** £24.45; **7** 11 tanks
costing £506; **8** Fiona's train by 4.38m

P63 **How big is the angle?** **1(a)** 30° **(b)** 72° **(c)** 94°
(d) 22° **(e)**109° **(f)**127°

P64 **Battleships** No answers

P65 **Dream playground** No answers

P66 **Entertainment!** Bowling and burger costs
£52.44; cinema and pizza costs £52.50;
cheaper option saves 6p

P67 **Bedroom furniture** No answers

P68 **Carpet fitter** 4m (no joins): £481.38 + £48.76
(underlay) = £530.14; if joins are used, answers
will vary. Most economical option is 3m carpet ×
8.5m with three joins £432.23 + £48.76
(underlay) = £480.99

Block E

P71 **How long?**

Journey	Time started	Time finished	Time taken
Home to school	8.10am	8.35am	**25 minutes**
School to home	3.15pm	**3.40pm**	25 minutes
To friend's house	**3.55pm**	4.18pm	23 minutes
To swimming pool	**6.05pm**	6.40pm	35 minutes

2 Day 1: 4 hours 50 mins; Day 2: 4 hours 50
mins; Day 3: 6 hours 35 mins; Day 4: 5 hours 40
mins; Day 5: he arrives at his destination at
5.50pm

P72 **Measure up** **1** 10; **2** 4; **3(a)** 6 hours 25
minutes **(b)** 5 hours 5 minutes **(c)** 1 hour 15
minutes; **4(a)** £23.85 **(b)** 85 fruit juices; 62
pots of raisins; **5(a)** Perimeter: 154m **(b)** Area:
780m² **(c)** 26 minutes; **6** Ingredients for 180:
4050g flour; 2025g butter; 1980g caster
sugar; 27 eggs; 675g jam; 1575g icing sugar;
18 tbsp water

P73 **Superleague**

Christchurch	8	6	2	0	33	18	20	15
Rushall	9	6	1	2	38	14	19	24
Hamworthy	9	5	4	0	35	18	19	17
Burnham	9	4	4	1	25	21	16	4
Bloomfield	7	4	1	2	30	26	13	4
Cleeve	9	3	4	2	21	23	13	−2
Maldon	9	2	5	2	14	31	11	−17
Blanford	9	2	4	3	18	29	10	−11

1 Christchurch; **2** Rushall; **3** Maldon; **4** Rushall;
5 Maldon; **6** Christchurch and Hamworthy

Homework answers

P74 **Baking time** *Three people:* 3 eggs, 180g butter, 330g flour, 180g currants, 90g sugar, 90ml milk; *Five people:* 5 eggs, 300g butter, 550g flour, 300g currants, 150g sugar, 150ml milk. **1** 2; **2** 25g; **3** 250g; **4** 120g; **5** 100ml

P75 **What do we need?** **1** (Chicken legs = £31.60) + (burgers = £18.20) + (sausages = £7.50) + (baps = £5.25) + (salad = £14.85) + (tomato sauce and brown sauce = £5) = £82.40;
2 150 × £2.50 = £375, profit: £375 − £82.40 = £292.60;
3 £82.40 ÷ £2.50 = 32.96; round up: 33 tickets

P76 **Equal match** $^3/_6 = {}^5/_{10}$; $^3/_4 = 0.75$; $0.25 = {}^1/_4$; $^{10}/_{10} = {}^8/_8$; $^3/_5 = 0.6$; $^3/_8 = {}^6/_{16}$; $^9/_{10} = 0.9$; $^4/_{10} = 0.4$

P77 **Match it** $^{10}/_7 = 1^3/_7$; $^{32}/_9 = 3^5/_9$; $^{38}/_{16} = 2^6/_{16}$; $^{37}/_5 = 7^2/_5$; $^{49}/_{12} = 4^1/_{12}$; $^{47}/_9 = 5^2/_9$; $^{15}/_7 = 2^1/_7$; $^{29}/_5 = 5^4/_5$; $^{63}/_{12} = 5^3/_{12}$; $^{36}/_{16}$ and $3^4/_{16}$ don't match ($^{36}/_{16} = 2^4/_{16}$ and $3^4/_{16} = {}^{52}/_{16}$)

P78 **Percentage maker** **1** *25%:* 60 = 15; 80 = 20; 120 = 30; 68 = 17; 200 = 50
2 *75%:* £500 = £375; 180 = 135; 320cm = 240cm; 96 = 72; £1.60 = £1.20
3 *15%:* 100 = 15; 600 = 90; £4.60 = £0.69; £75 = £11.25; 1600 = 240
4 *60%:* £1760 = £1056; £1.50 = £0.90; 320 = 192; 15 metres = 9 metres; 25 = 15

P79 **All in a day** Answers will vary

P80 **Family bingo** The winner is Mrs Bonus

P81 **A good read**

Bookshop	Author	Month	Book type
Bargain Read	James Eagle	March	Science fiction
Choice Books	Sheila Sparrow	January	Adventure
Super Bookstore	George Gull	April	Biography

P82 **Magic 4 × 4s** Answers will vary

P83 **High Street** *Sale bargains:* Bike: £95 - £14.25 = £80.75; Jeans: £10.50 - £1.05 = £9.45; Camera: £40 - £4 = £36; Trainers: £24.99 - £5 = £19.99; Watch: £25 - £5 = £20; Radio: £45.98 − £11.50 = £34.48; TV: £150 − £7.50 = £142.50; Computer monitor: £99 − £4.95 = £94.05. *Building Society:* David £10 + £1.50 = £11.50; Jamil £24 + £3.60 = £27.60; Sunita £18 + £2.70 = £20.70; Sarah £56 + £8.40 = £64.40; Emma £37 + £5.55 = £42.55; Sanjay £105 + £15.75 = £120.75.

P84 **Fraction match** A7; B4; C9; D6; E3; F10; G8; H2; I5; J1

P85 **Four fractions in a row**

$\frac{1}{4}$	$\frac{3}{4}$	$\frac{2}{4}$	$\frac{1}{2}$
$\frac{1}{2}$	$\frac{2}{4}$	$\frac{3}{4}$	$\frac{1}{4}$
$\frac{3}{4}$	$\frac{1}{4}$	$\frac{1}{2}$	$\frac{2}{4}$
$\frac{2}{4}$	$\frac{1}{2}$	$\frac{1}{4}$	$\frac{3}{4}$

P86 **Sale now on!** Coat £105; handbag £55.25; shoes £35.10; dining table £280; sofa £451.50 Daniel pays £643.72 for a dining table and a sofa

P87 **Written methods** **1** 1251; **2** 1354; **3** 218; **4** 2672; **5** 469; **6** 246; **7** 3816; **8** 6786; **9** 2024; **10** 213; **11** 128 remainder 5; **12** 0

P88 **You're the teacher!** *Correct answers:* Question numbers 2, 3, 6, 8, 9, 12, 13; *Correct answers to other questions should be:* **1** 521; **4** 0.428; **5** 213; **7** 5490; **10** 9.93; **11** 45.6; **14** 2.91; **15** 2030

Puzzles and problems answers

1   **Chilly Billy** 47 degrees
2   **What's the question?** Answers will vary
3   **What's my number?** 12
4   **School long jump** 3.145m
5   **Texting totals** £28.20
6   **On the river** £1.90 each
7   **That's square, man!** 36 and 64
8   **Prime time** 89
9   **Parallel lines** 3
10 **Kite design** 11
11 **Algy and Brian** 13
12 **Prove Penny wrong**

13 **Guilders for Gail** 1200
14 **Seven-loving Sven** 20
15 **Happy hundred!** Answers should be around 32,480 for an 11-year-old
16 **Car colours survey** Answers will vary
17 **Tea breaks** 1.65 litres
18 **Christmas turkey** The turkey weighs 15.4 pounds. It needs to be cooked for 5 hours and 28 minutes
19 **How likely?** **1** impossible **2** unlikely **3** likely **4** impossible **5** certain
20 **Invisible ink** 375ml
21 **Goal!** 55
22 **Pick 'n' mix** 250g
23 **Swimming pool** 56m
24 **Fish 'n' chips** 60p
25 **Model plane** 8.64m
26 **In the middle** 1.15m
27 **Moon traveller** 240,000 miles
28 **Pizza delivery** 2¼ mini pizzas each
29 **Battle of the bands** Kneecap makes the most money by £2.75

30 **Fruit punch** 4.5 litres lemonade, 12 oranges, 9 limes, 600g sugar, 900g strawberries
31 **Blewett Hall** 20,000
32 **Haunted cellar** 125
33 **Peckish peacocks** 500g
34 **Jumping Jacks** 265cm
35 **Sponsored silence** £140
36 **Cut-price car** £480

SCHOLASTIC

Also available in this series:

ISBN 978-1407-10216-0

ISBN 978-1407-10217-7

ISBN 978-1407-10218-4

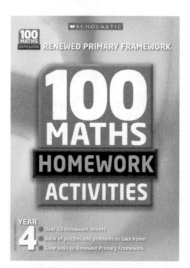

ISBN 978-1407-10219-1

ISBN 978-1407-10220-7

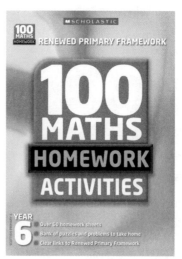

ISBN 978-1407-10221-4

To find out more, call: 0845 603 9091
or visit our website www.scholastic.co.uk